C000274596

It's Never Too Late To Look Great!

Biography

Maggie worked as a newspaper reporter and commercial writer for many years before taking up a second career as owner of dress shops in Broadway and Stow on the Wold. From her home in the Cotswolds she continues to write about fashion, and is passionate about helping older women find their own individual style.

IT'S NEVER TOO LATE TO LOOK GREAT!

Style for the Young-at-Heart

Maggie Cox

Copyright © 2019 Maggie Cox

The moral right of the author has been asserted.

Apart from any fair dealing for the purposes of research or private study,
or criticism or review, as permitted under the Copyright, Designs and Patents
Act 1988, this publication may only be reproduced, stored or transmitted, in
any form or by any means, with the prior permission in writing of the
publishers, or in the case of reprographic reproduction in accordance with
the terms of licences issued by the Copyright Licensing Agency. Enquiries
concerning reproduction outside those terms should be sent to the publishers.

Matador
9 Priory Business Park,
Wistow Road, Kibworth Beauchamp,
Leicestershire. LE8 0RX
Tel: 0116 279 2299
Email: books@troubador.co.uk
Web: www.troubador.co.uk/matador
Twitter: @matadorbooks

ISBN 978 1789016 826

British Library Cataloguing in Publication Data.
A catalogue record for this book is available from the British Library.

Printed and bound by CPI Group (UK) Ltd, Croydon, CR0 4YY
Typeset in 12pt Adobe Garamond Pro by Troubador Publishing Ltd, Leicester, UK

Matador is an imprint of Troubador Publishing Ltd

To friends and colleagues who were so generous with advice, and going in front of my camera. And to my husband, who is still my husband, after endless pestering for technical, computer related, answers.

Contents

GETTING STARTED

1

How it Began

Stepping over Snakes

You gotta have style.
It helps you get down the stairs.
It helps you get up in the morning.
It's a way of life. Without it, you're nobody.

— Diana Vreeland

I was in the Amazonian rainforest preparing to go on a survival course with the Brazilian army, part of a cruise up the Amazon on the Swan Hellenic ship, *Minerva*. 'Pull up your socks over your trousers,' they said. 'There're snakes and mosquitoes everywhere.'

I looked over to Judith, one of our ship-board travelling companions. No socks. Pretty trainers and skinny jeans. 'This is absolutely as far as I go. Flat shoes are bad enough. But socks. No way,' she protested. Sockless, she marched forward to savour the delights of the jungle. And indeed, we all, including Judith, survived unbitten and unmolested by insect or reptile after two hours in the green, steamy heat of the rainforest.

Judith's aversion to socks didn't come as a surprise. Socks aren't top of the packing list for a woman who is rarely seen in flat shoes. She wears four-inch heels for most occasions. They accentuate her tall, slim figure, and she has a pair for every outfit. She walks like a model, as well she should, because in her pre-Amazonian existence she had strutted the catwalk, as well as qualifying and practising as an architect.

Judith, the inspiration for this book on board her husband's motor yacht, *Vivace*

Judith is a woman of style. Now retired, aged 76, she continues to wear beautifully put together outfits for every occasion, whether she's cooking, entertaining, gardening, partying or crewing their 44-foot motor yacht across the sea from Guernsey where they live. How, I thought, could even a little bit of this style rub off on me?

Although I've tried to dress with flair throughout my life, I've always been impressed by women who seem to do the style thing as if it was as natural as brushing your teeth. Women who shine with confidence, knowing they look as good as they possibly can. And Judith is one of those women.

Next to Judith my number two idol is Cleopatra. The legendary Egyptian queen seduced Mark Antony, the Roman General, in her mature years. She was not conventionally beautiful but she was bright and charming. She probably spoke several languages, and was a brilliant conversationalist. This set her apart from other women.

As well as her positive attitude towards people and the world in which she lived, she was very aware of the importance of her appearance. For ceremonial events she dressed as the goddess Isis to enhance her authority, and for her coin image she chose to show a strong jaw line like her father. Shakespeare left us the memorable lines:

'Age cannot wither her nor custom stale her infinite variety. Other women cloy the appetites they feed, but she makes hungry where most she satisfies.'

How reassuring for us young-at-hearters today. Cleopatra was a mature woman when she seduced Antony in her late thirties (this was old in her time!), not conventionally beautiful, but utterly charming. And of course she dressed in a way that set her apart.

But what about those of us who don't have good cheekbones like Cleopatra or tall, slim figures like Judith and have never learned to walk like a model? We less-than-perfect mortals, on the top of all this, have wrinkles and lumpy bits to cope with! Can we even get on to the style starting blocks? Yes, I believe we can.

However. We vibrant want-to-be-Judiths have a problem. Fashion culture is about youth. There is little for us over fifties. Style guides target the young, or if not the young, those who with some tweaking of diet, underwear, hair colour or botox, can fit into the young mould. Our culture rejoices in the young. 'And why not?' you may ask. In many ways this is wonderful. Young is energetic, attractive, and full of ambition. But this isn't much help for us more mature women, whose knees are a bit knobbly, who are reluctant to bare too much arm, bosom or thigh and who can't necessarily cinch our waists or squeeze into skinnies.

Mainstream fashion designs aim to be sexy, eccentric, brightly patterned, coy, even childish, with frayed edges and crazy silhouettes. We see young, pouting models in top magazines who look as if they need, but are banned from having, a good meal. Their clothes are often obscured by the noir, sexy image the photographer wants, and you know the frustration of seeing what you think is a great dress, but the image only shows the back – and in moody shadow. Seventy-year-old models do appear occasionally on the catwalk. But these are exceptions, and older women still face barriers in getting jobs, being authority figures – and catching the waiter's eye!

The emphasis on youthful clothes is part of a wider culture that undervalues the old, and particularly older women. If we're not careful we become invisible – and this despite the fact that there're 12 million of us in the UK over the age of fifty, we spend £350 billion a year – and we're more healthy and active than ever before. And we do not want invisibility.

We want, and need, to stay a part of the modern world. We want the gravitas of a well-paid job or the freedom to freelance and pick and choose, but above all, we want to take part in life, to be consulted, to work, to play, to enjoy. And to wear eye-catching, flattering clothes that bring us out of the shadows – not only a joy in itself, but, as you'll find out, has lots of benefits for our well-being and self-confidence.

So let's throw open our wardrobe doors – and tell our clothes they had better watch out. New rivals will be on the way if they don't come up to scratch. We can't compete with the giraffe-necked nineteen-year-old, but we can reinvent ourselves with clothes that flatter and make us stand out from the crowd.

But where to find new and exciting clothes? We read magazines, newspapers, see what the celebrities are wearing and just get confused. Advice is contradictory. Trends appear, are then rubbished. New ideas, new shapes, new colours, new directions come and go in a flash. Black is in. Black is out. Brown is the new black. Grey is the new black. Match your bag to your shoes. Never match your bag to your shoes. Skinny jeans are in. Bootleg is coming back, maybe. Pastels, yes, no. Brights, yes, no. Tight frocks are hot, not hot.

The clothes displayed in shops, catalogues and internet sites promise instant transformation. 'Wear me and you'll be on trend,' they say. But we of the older generation can't do this. We can't put on the latest fashion garment and look good, let alone stylish. Short frilly skirts – too girlish. Frayed jeans, too teenage. Metallics – only good for *Star Wars*. Tightly fitted dresses – too revealing. Bright florals – save for the garden or curtains. What we want is to look like stylish, fashionable grown-ups.

The more we search, the more questions bubble up. What kind of outfits are we looking for? How do we know what things from the young culture we can still wear? Do we have to play down our previous ideas of dressing or completely rethink what to wear?

And what are we aiming at. What does 'good style' actually mean? It's certainly not 'fashion' which is churned out twice or four times a year according to what the design doyens think will drive sales.

I still have a passion for clothes, and want to revamp my look and help others to reinvent themselves. But, as more sags and wrinkles bounce back from the mirror, is there a new style path I, and my contemporaries, should be following?

I've always loved bright colours. Do they have to go? I've always chosen unusual, edgy clothes. No more? Dramatic, or glamorous looks? Are they still appropriate? Can I wear purple? Should I blend into the background in dark or beige clothes, and keep my mouth shut? The latter, difficult, as my husband will vouch.

One thing I'm sure of is that I don't intend to give up on style, and certainly not now, having seen how Judith dresses, and noticed the attention she gets when she walks into a room.

And I know that clothes are fun – the whole business of planning, shopping and wearing outfits. It's part of our everyday lives, and especially exciting when we find a new shop – will there be something there to die for, or at least push our credit card to the limit for?

I also know from years of exploring what to wear, when you get it right, and you know you look good, you *feel* good. And if you're having a bad day, a particular outfit or a flattering colour can give you a boost and actually make you feel better.

This is the challenge for us baby boomers. The only thing I'm sure about for the moment is that if you get it right, good style gets you compliments. Not, 'Have you lost weight?' (Subtext, 'You look less fat than usual.') Or, 'You're thinner,' (meaning you look scraggy, or unhealthy). Nor do you want, 'Have you found a new hairdresser?' (which means your red streak looks terrible). Or, 'You look fresh,' (in other words, 'Your eye bags don't look quite so bad'). What you really want are comments like, 'You look great,' or 'I love what you're wearing,' or 'How sexy is that,' (if that's what you intended!).

I began by travelling around the Cotswolds, and later further afield. Whenever I visited a new town I devoured the high street, shopping centres and independent boutiques searching for inspiration. Up and down I went, round and round rails of too dazzling, too short, too frilly clothes screaming, 'Buy me, buy me' until my head was spinning, and all I wanted was coffee and a dark room. I knew many of the clothes are geared to the young, but there must be something for me!

Well, who would believe it? Masses of clothes, eye-watering choice, and all you come home with is a headache.

I started to think hard about the challenge of style for us young-at-hearters, and an idea began to take shape in my mind. I remembered how stylish is my friend Pauline Daniels, actor, singer and comedian. She's a true star of the stage. And I recalled all the extraordinary women I'd met on my journey. They're also **STAR**s in the way they dress. They're all **Surprising, True** to themselves, **Artistic**, and know how to **Reinvent** themselves.

They have the **STAR** qualities needed for real style.

Surprise

A stylish woman is surprising because she hits the button which says 'I know how to be different.' And she has the imagination to wear something unusual and not to be a fashion clone.

True to Yourself

Some of our personality, our true self – our likes and dislikes, what we do, or have done – is somehow revealed by how we present ourselves when we get style right.

Artistry

Artistry, or a touch of flair, is the ability to choose appealing outfits. If your choice of crazy hat looks like a hedgehog it might surprise, but not with admiration. It has to be different, but also beautiful in some way.

Reinvention

And every stylish woman manages to look contemporary, reinventing herself from time to time in some way. She's not a fashion clone. But she shows she's of the moment.

But before we get further into this, I decided to start by looking around the streets for young-at-hearters who have tried hard – but just got it wrong. My thinking was that if we really, really know what we *don't* want, it'll be easier to work out what we do want.

These are the 'Ugh!' (I wouldn't be seen dead in that) looks coming up next.

2

Ugh!

What Doesn't Work

What 'normal' people perceive as ugly,
I can usually see something of beauty in it.
– Alexander McQueen

We've all tut-tutted about what we think is bad taste, or 'inappropriate' dress for the occasion. And I've heard many times, 'I know what I *don't* want.' So I'll show you some horrors I've seen lately. Looking at what makes us shudder can point to new options.

Here are some of my 'Ugh!' looks.

Exploding Paint Box

An outfit with in-your-face colours, usually with at least two or three brights – say red, purple and lime, with extra shades, clashing or complementary, thrown in for good (bad?) measure. The block colour trend is responsible for some of this, and floral or geometric prints also sometimes get into the act. Can be a nostalgic refusal to give up the past, 'I got lots of compliments in the sixties when I mixed these colours and patterns,' or a subconscious plea: 'This is the only way I seem to get attention,' (also see Cruella de Vil below).

Unabridged colour when we're young makes us glow with vitality. When we're older, its exuberance can overwhelm and highlights our fragility.

Lampshade

'I don't like my shape, so I'll hide it.' The aim of this look is to go for as big a shape as possible so that no one will guess what's underneath. Couture catwalks have been known to produce an exact copy of the classic lampshade shape, rounded at the top getting gradually bigger as it drops down, with a circular bone around the bottom so that the dress can be animated by the model to move like a dalek. This extreme version isn't seen in shops, but appears as voluminous kaftans or oversized tops.

Often associated with exotic prints that are believed to fool the onlooker that trim perfection is underneath.

Does not disguise size. It implies rotundity – whether the body underneath is generous or slim.

Tent in a Hurricane

An extreme version of the above. Often occurs when the 'lampshade' wants to glamorise the look by adding lots of flappy bits – a loose waterfall jacket, long floaty scarf, free-falling bandeau or headscarf. It can also include a large, floppy brimmed hat.

Not only does this imply out of control curves, but the flappy bits exaggerate the already wide silhouette.

'Tent in a hurricane'.

Badly Packed Parachute

Usually, but not always, associated with generous curves, when unexpected bits of flesh pop out. The protagonist takes full marks for trying hard. The outfit's been chosen with an eye for the latest fashion, with contemporary shape and quality fabric. But size is misjudged, and there's hope over expectation that the body hasn't changed shape in ten/twenty/thirty years.

Christmas Tree

The over-decorated look. Can often be the fault of designers who frill-up tailored jackets, or put zebras with sparkle on tee shirts, or firmly attach a (never to be removed) floral bouquet to the front of a dress or jumper. But we can easily do this all by ourselves when a single embellishment gets revved up by a 'more is better' impulse. It can start with a bold necklace. Then there's a contrast scarf and

'Over-decorated Christmas tree'.

fancy belt that might fit in. And what about the new leopard shoes and designer bag we've just bought? All the accessories are beautiful in their own right, so together they must enhance the style. Big mistake. One or two accessories add chic. Too many, and they take over.

Often associated with 'keeping up with the fashion pack'.

Cruella de Vil

It's the cartoon persona I mean in *One Hundred and One Dalmatians*. Forget about the kidnapping of puppies! Cruella is the diva of all divas. It is the look that could just have come off the stage, characterised by layers of bold, outrageous patterns and bright colours, and voluminous enough to be swished for dramatic entrances. Garments are usually ankle length and always over accessorised, with lips and eyes made up from breakfast to bed. (I was once told off by my husband for wearing a red, tulip-shaped coat to meet friends in a local bar. 'Save it for the theatre', he said.)

Tends to occur when we young-at-hearters think we're being ignored by designers (too many young style clothes), or by the world at large (why was my, very sensible, dinner table comment ignored?) The look says, 'I'm not invisible,' but says it much too loudly.

The tendency can also result from over-compensating for an artistic temperament which has been crushed by the everyday demands of life whose only dramas are a blocked sink, or a washing machine that breaks down mid-cycle.

Wrinkly Teenager

Dare we think the Mutton and Lamb words? Well, probably. Trying too hard to be Peter (or Petula) Pan. Squeezing into the latest skater (formerly called A-line) skirt. Cutting holes in jeans. Tottering on six-inch platforms. Fortunately not seen very often in the young-at-heart community, but can be scary if suddenly spotted.

'Wrinkly teenager'.

Flesh Flash

A variant of the above with the addition of bared midriff, boobs (partial), back or thighs, or any combination of these. Shoulders can be excluded on the grounds that they usually survive the ravages of bodily collapse.

Fashion Junky

Must have the latest four-times-a-year fashion hit – red stilettos, snakeskin-effect anything, long, shiny pleated skirt, velvet trousers, bell-sleeved dress, leopard jeggings. Rare, but sometimes occurs in cities where the urge to have 'street cred' becomes compulsive. Often associated with an addiction to shopping, and the inability to come out of a dress shop empty-handed.

Footballer's Wife

See above, but add 'most expensive' and 'must include encrusted jewels'. Mostly seen in wealthy suburbs.

Would-Be Goth

Relies heavily on make-up. Particularly 1970's eyes – false lashes, heavy black eyeliner going up at the corners. Sometimes lips are too strongly outlined. Or painted in the darkest red. With the younger of us, this tendency includes wearing a lot of black which features lace panelling and sheer organza overlays. Outfits can be low cut or with a Victorian, chin-hugging neckline.

The fully integrated Goth bride or Goth princess aren't usually seen in our community of young-at-hearters, but scary Goth eyes or too much black lace occasionally appear.

Grandad's Baggy Cardigan

This is the grandmother version of the 'earth mother' look, linked with living in the country, lots of children, and dogs and cats (rescue). Key look is well-worn joggers, loose jumpers and dark cardis (with holes), or old floral dresses, to enable water and paint games to be played on the floor with grandchildren.

It can also be an anti-fashion statement. 'Bring back Laura Ashley smocks. I can't stand all these new-fangled unisex clothes'.

Grunge

Grunge was the name given to punk-rock and heavy-metal bands of the nineties. They were rebels in music – and in clothes. They wore a lot of flannel and cast-offs (unwashed). The aim was to look, well, grungy.

The signature look now is dark charity-shop trousers and tops, possibly paint (and other) stained, or even a (very) old shell suit. Can also be a carefully assembled style. I'm making a statement: 'I don't care what I look like. I'm not part of this throw-away society.' Or it can be totally unselfconscious as in, 'Why would I care what I look like?'

There's still a bit of this about, even with us young-at-hearters. You want to say, 'Have you been gardening, or tried to look like a scarecrow?'

Lady of the Manor

Total reverse of the above. Twin-set and pearls continue to be the wardrobe staple, together with knee-length box pleats, frilly-edged cardigans and pink pussy-bow blouses. Hyacinth Bucket comes to mind with her fussy, floral blouses and skirts, and carefully colour-matched hats. Never would cleavage be remotely hinted at, and an accidental ankle display would be carefully avoided by the appropriate sitting posture, lower legs neatly crossed underneath the chair.

This is a look frozen from the fifties, and, possibly, an 'I-am-better-than-you' attitude.

Note. Actual ladies of the manor have long since dropped this look for a contemporary 'woman-of-the-people' style.

Las Vegas Casino Sign

A fluorescent-coloured garment is the centre piece here. Could be bright leggings teamed with stripy top, or vice versa, that sparkle and flash like a neon sign. One spotted recently on a seaside promenade consisted of iridescent orange tights, orange and red stripy top and silver sparkly bag and shoes. A more genteel version would be a bright fuchsia dress, with clashing orange, high-gloss stilettos. Not very common unless on holiday, or when there's bright sunshine.

Wearing bright colours, especially in sunshine, is invigorating. Vibrating like a neon sign is best left to courting birds in the jungle.

Grieving Widow

We've been told over and over again by magazine editors, 'You can never go wrong with black. It's slimming. It's chic.' This is all very well when we're young but not necessarily now. This tendency puts any unshapely cardigan or nondescript dress on a pedestal because it's black. Usually worn without decoration or embellishment.

But do we want to look like an elderly Mediterranean-village widow, who wears black for evermore after the death of her husband?

Leopardarama

The extreme animal print look. Is characterised by two or more different-sized patterns, in un-animal colours – pink, blue, orange or fuchsia. Can include leopard-look tights or leggings, and shirts in giant zebra stripes. Looked appropriate behind the bar in seventies soaps.

Dreary Dearie

Any of the above, or actually anything, that's worn with boredom or misery – hunched shoulders, downward gaze, never a hint of a smile. The walk is usually painfully slow even though there's no impairment, and it takes courage to approach this type for fear of 'catching' the blues.

Now you know my pet hates. Are you, mostly, with me? I hope so.

But with fashion nothing should be totally off limits, and we all have different preferences. Alexander McQueen, the British fashion designer and couturier whose work was always bold, often controversial, ruled nothing out. And I've taken to heart his belief that there's beauty, somewhere, in everything. Most of my 'Ugh!' looks aren't *all* bad. They've taken a good idea, and run with it… just a little too vigorously.

Except… Dreary Dearie! She doesn't see the good side of anything. She doesn't rate herself as important – she has no 'attitude'. But by this I don't mean wilful belligerence, or bloody-mindedness. I mean the spirit which fires us up and gets us out of bed in the morning. Or, simply, the way we approach life. Is the glass half full, or half empty? It's how we present ourselves. However beautiful is our outfit, we have to wear it well or it'll count for nothing. We'll have a lot to say about this later.

But now back to 'style'. It's a word we hear a dozen times a day to describe just about anything from pictures to palaces, but what does it mean in the world of fashion?

When we say, 'Look at that woman over there, she's got real style,' what are we getting at? I have already told you about my four STAR qualities, so let's start exploring these ideas right now.

3

STAR Style
The Big Four

Fashions fade. Style is eternal.

— Yves Saint Laurent

The outstanding women I've met – owners of boutiques and their customers have all found their own personal 'eternal' style as Yves Saint Laurent put it. They're not crazy followers of fashion. They've found a 'look' (or several looks) that suits them, makes them stand out from the crowd.

So have the many stylish older women we see in magazines – actresses, designers and fashionistas. Think of Charlotte Rampling's sleek masculine, but sexy, tailored look, Helen Mirren's elegant fitted gowns and Iris Apfel's crazily arty outfits always topped with extraordinary glasses. Apfel, the American interior designer and fashion icon, was never out of the headlines even in her nineties.

And they all use the four STAR qualities. Remember them from the first chapter?

Surprise

True to Yourself

Artistry

Reinvention

So let's see what they mean.

To surprise is to be different, to be original, so that we grab attention in a flash, but not – at our age! – like a firework display, or a metal-clad alien, or an over-hairy leopard. We can surprise by wearing *one* remarkable thing like a quirky hat, or unusual jewellery, or like several rows of pearls worn low, or behind your neck, or an outfit that goes head to toe in one flattering colour. Whatever it is, it will be head-turning.

A big, funky stole over a
simple cream coat – Surprise.

If you're sporty –
be 'True to Yourself'.

To be true to yourself is to show *something* of your personality in your clothes. You have to look the part. If you put on the latest sporty jumpsuit you need to look relaxed, and feel comfortable standing with legs apart rather than posed one in front of the other. If you've never so much as thrown a ball, or worn a pair of jeans, you're probably going to look shifty, as though you've forgotten your handbag. You have to connect, at least in spirit, with wild open spaces to look authentic in a sporty outfit.

And it's no good sprawling around, limbs all over the place, if you're trying to make the most of an elegant dress. This could happen if you're trying to force yourself into a way of posh dressing which doesn't suit you.

Style has to be more than just a collection of clothes and accessories. Your real personality – though not *every* aspect of it – needs to be on display. When you see someone and immediately think, 'I bet she's an artist,' or, 'She's obviously seen a lot of the world,' or even, 'She must be a tax inspector!' – that person is obviously dressing in a way that reflects something of what they are inside.

Now artistry. You may think this is a step too far. That we're getting too ambitious, too pretentious, too far into the realms of Michelangelo. But just listen.

We all have *some* aesthetic talents. Every time we put flowers in water we're using this flair. We're bringing together pleasing blooms, blending colours and making an attractive form. Every time we admire a landscape or moon-shadows, or stop to look at a church or an impressive skyscraper, we're tuning in to our artistic side.

'Artistic'.

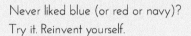

Never liked blue (or red or navy)?
Try it. Reinvent yourself.

Reinvention. We know now that style isn't fashion. Fashion is what is churned out four times a year, and style is what we choose, from the fashion mix, to give ourselves a unique image. But we still have to keep an eye on what is new (and pleasing) in the current fashion scene and incorporate it in some way into the way we dress.

Hmm, I can hear you say, 'This style business sounds like an uphill trudge. You're telling me I've got to be an artist. I have to find 'surprising' things from all the youthful froth you've told me is out there. I have to watch fashion trends, but not get obsessed by them. On top of this, I need to have 'personality' – and flaunt it. That's too hard!'

But that's what this book is about – to show that we're all capable of style if we go step by step, looking at one thing at a time. And our journey will reveal the ways and means of finding our unique, attractive look that brings admiration and confidence.

While my STAR style qualities hold good for any age, I'm the first to admit it gets a bit trickier for us young-at-hearters. We can't surprise by exposing new bits of body parts (we might well want to keep more and more of those out of sight!), or by tottering on the latest six-inch platforms or stilettos – those are strictly for the perfectly balanced who don't look as if they're about to fall over any minute. And nor do we want to look 'like mutton dressed as lamb' which, as my friend Stephanie, teacher, musician and flower-lover, says is her worst fear, and one that's shared by all of us.

And it doesn't help that most of us perky oldies have to make do with bodies that have suffered at least some of the ravages of time – or over indulgence. Who hasn't complained about being too hippy, too scraggy, or not having enough hair, or having too much hair (that everyone else would die for, but we don't want!). We know full well we're not as shapely, waisted and flab-free as we once were, so that eye-catching and well-fitting clothes are more difficult for us to find.

But, hang on, we're all flawed. That's what we human beings are. Imperfect! (You probably know that if our faces were exactly symmetrical we would look odd, not beautiful. This becomes clear when a photograph is digitally manipulated to use the same side of the face twice, by reversing one side in the same picture.) So it's reassuring to keep that in mind, even though it may take us young-at-hearters a bit more time and effort to get the four STAR principles right, we *can* get them right.

We don't want to give the impression we're trying to be twenty, or even twenty years younger, but we want to surprise and delight in our own way. And we still can, as we'll discover on our journey.

Here's our mission – to create a look that will separate us from the crowd. Think of Audrey Hepburn (let's put the bar high). She created a new style – 'elegant simplicity' – which made her one of the style icons of all time. In the fifties when full skirts and big patterns were headline news, she wore simple, fitted black trousers and flats and slash neck tee shirts. And in the film *Sabrina*, 1954, her simple cocktail dress with fitted bodice and boat neckline heralded the start of the Little Black Dress, popular ever since. Then in *Breakfast at Tiffany's* came the image we all associate with her. The long, black, sleeveless sheath dress which she wore with masses of pearls and long gloves – together with the long cigarette holder – set its time in stone.

She had discovered she looked best in sleek, simple dresses which went against the contemporary trend of full skirts and exuberant patterns. A true mistress of *reinvention* and *surprise*. Her outfits provided a perfect foil for her tall, slim figure and elfin looks so she was *true to herself*. She was always neat and well-groomed, always wearing lots of black, blues and greys that suited her dark colouring, often with a large, black brimmed hat – and she was never without oversized sunglasses. Her *artistry* made her an icon. She caused a sensation then, and inspires us now. And it's worth saying that Audrey Hepburn didn't see herself as beautiful – because of the bump on her nose and because her feet were too big.

Of course it isn't as easy for us as it was for the talented Audrey Hepburn. She probably knew instinctively what shape of clothes and hats to go for, how her clothes needed to suit her bodily proportions and lifestyle and the colours that were right for her. We have to do some work to get there, but there'll be many rewards if we take this seriously. Quickly cast your eye down the following and take heart.

- **The right clothes give us more confidence.** Outfits that flatter and bring compliments make us feel good about ourselves.
- **Style stimulates our creativity.** Just like painting a picture, decorating a room or arranging flowers, working out what to wear boosts our imagination. Keeps the little grey cells moving. And don't we need that!
- **A zingy outfit lifts our spirits** when we're feeling down – not by indulging in retail therapy, although that can help – but by putting on colours that are uplifting – red for confidence, and yellow for cheerfulness for example. This is well-proven psychology. More of this later.
- **Well-loved garments keep the past alive.** I've kept a silvery-grey linen jumper I wore for my second wedding thirteen years ago. I still wear it sometimes. It brings a beautiful day back to me. My friend Jan has kept a tweedy jacket from the sixties, because it reminds her of a special date but also because she still looks good in it.

- **Clothes let us play games.** A former colleague of mine said to me one day: 'I can choose in the morning who I want to be. I can pretend I'm a model by wearing a long, lean dress with a perky hat. If I layer a trendy top over skinny jeans and hide under my biggest sunglasses, I can be a celebrity.'
- **Style is fun.** There's delight in shopping (more later) and pleasure when we can surprise other people.
- **When you look good you'll attract new friends.** Whenever my friend Andree goes out and about, people will start to talk to her because of her appearance. Whether in jeans or a smart dress she looks like a model – even though she's never been on a catwalk. She just knows how to put things together. Young and old start conversations with her, and she always comes home with life histories of people she's met.
- **And not least, style might change your life!** As a late dear friend of mine once said, 'When you step out of the door you never know who you'll meet. So you'd better make each day count.'

But, even better, we can bring something completely new to the world. We're each unique. That's not changed from when we were toddlers to now, in our maturity. No one has exactly the same colouring, body shape, facial contours and *character*. So there's a special look for each of us to find. And how exciting is that! We can be a one-off in the way we dress. We can be unique by how we present ourselves.

So now the work begins as we look at how we can turn four principles into something that's going to transform us into style STARS. First a closer look at **S**urprise.

SURPRISE

1

Wow!

Is it a Bird? Is it a Plane? No, it's a Hat

Surprise is the greatest gift which life can grant us.
— Boris Pasternak

A woman went out shopping.
Tried on an amazing hat.
Bought it.
Got compliments.
Started to smile more.
Walked with a spring in her step.
Wore it for a party.
A man approached, said, 'What an unusual hat'.
She married him.

This is a story told by American psychologist Professor Karen Pine. The woman, Meg, had found an amazing hat that turned heads. It was her Surprise.

The hat was not directly responsible for Meg finding a husband (don't try this on your next shopping trip!) but was a catalyst for change. The woman was tempted, out of her comfort zone, to

A striking hat always surprises.

buy something crazy, but which suited her and brought her lots of compliments. Whenever she wore it she felt more confident than she had ever done before, and showed it in the way she moved and talked to people. At a party, a man was immediately attracted to her, and had to find out more about the woman who could choose such an individual hat. The relationship developed into marriage.

Meg was a style STAR. She had succeeded with a single, surprising accessory which made her stand out from the crowd. It had made her unique.

So, here's our first, and maybe easiest way, to take advantage of the Surprise principle. To focus on the detail. One idea is to take your best feature – and make it better with an eye-catching accessory. This means you'll be drawing attention to one of your good-to-look-at assets, with something also pleasing on the eye. A win-win strategy.

Can I hear you say all your assets disappeared years ago? (Or you can't remember if you ever had any!) I'm here to say that this isn't true. You've probably been comparing yourself too harshly with the younger generation. Think hard, and I'm sure you'll come up with at least one physical feature to show off, and likely as not, many more.

The thing about a body is that it's a complicated thing. And we don't see all of it at once – not usually anyway! We're drawn to details. Great news for us young oldies because we can show off the best and make the rest disappear under semi-fitted, or flowing garments. Even though we don't have a perfect body (did we ever?) we can make the most of what we have (as we always tried to do).

Here are a few ideas. If you've got good legs, get them out and show them off with attractive wedges, flats or heels so that you can flash the, once risqué Victorian, ankle – and a little bit more. There's so much choice of footwear around, which is pretty *and* comfortable, so make the most of it. Then buy fancy or sleek tights to take the Surprise factor a step further.

If you have narrow hips, show them off. People will think you are slim all over.

If you have a waist, or can just about see where you had one once, for heavens sake emphasise it with an attractive, unusual belt. The rest of us will be green with envy. You can always be looking out for Surprise belts to add to your drawer.

If you have narrow hips, rejoice. Emphasising them will make your whole body look slim.

Whatever your shape, a funky, but beautiful scarf (leave pink leopards and purple zebras for the juniors) will always get you noticed.

Working on the same plan, challenged eyesight gets turned into an asset. Yours is the wonderful world of spectacles, which can transform your face with the right shape and colour, and hide a multitude of shadows and late-night (or well dug-in) puffiness – and give even a simple outfit a new edge. Be known for your collection. My husband keeps a spreadsheet for mine, and often says – 'Not another pair, you've topped last year's total already'.

A new, contemporary hair style turns heads. Not quite an accessory, but a cost-effective way to get noticed. Curly hair is a great asset, and as you get older it sometimes does gets curlier. Your Surprise can be a new, scrunched casual style. It's easy and fresh-looking. Thick wavy hair is a big bonus too. Even if you're always complaining that it never does what you want, consider it a blessing and spend money, and/or time on taming it. Then, if you dare, go for a completely new colour. Hair dyes and colouring techniques have come on so much in the last few years, that home or salon treatments can be transformative and head-turning.

Sticking to the make-the-best-of-the-body theme here are more ideas to bring on Surprise.

Cherish voluptuous cleavage. Don't squash it in, and button up to the neck. Not always anyway. Those of us who are less well endowed would give up their priority boarding passes to get one half of it. If necessary consider equity release – or at least raiding your holiday fund – for a good uplifting bra! Focus your Surprise on beautiful, low or lowish-cut tops. Even a hint of curve will give extra life to an even half decent top – and/or deflect the eye from bigger curves lower down.

Willowy height. Don't hide it. Clothes look better on tall women. Full stop. How often do you see short, stubby women on the catwalk? Wear high heels, there're plenty of comfy ones around, stand up straight and know you're elegant. You alone can wear any print you fancy, as big and bold as you like, and wide-leg trousers that make the rest of us look like daleks on castors. And, even though you may also be plump, you can wear expansive patterns and colours as long as you go for flowing styles. Exotic patterns can be your Surprise.

A petite body. If this is you, rejoice! Our 'young' culture spawns a multitude of stuff for lithesome figures. Ignore the outrageously flirty, cold-shoulder and bum-skimming offerings, and head for skinny jeans, soft, fitted jersey dresses and cropped tops. If you're tiny, you'll save pounds on samples, always in small sizes, and sales where only the tiniest outfits are left. You can gather armfuls of Surprises easier than picking up nuts in a market.

And there are more ways of getting the wow factor into your wardrobe.

A total, top to toe look can be your Surprise. You can stun your audience with total simplicity from head to ankle. No frills, no flounces, sticky-out bits or complicated jewellery. A well-cut, smooth flowing shift dress with matching, uncomplicated shoes and simple bag. Ultra simplicity of line is supremely elegant, and head-turning.

And then you can use colour. For instance, keeping your outfit to one electrifying, flattering colour will charm in an instant as will putting together an amazing colour *combination* – like orange-red with a touch of cerise, or cobalt with turquoise. Because this is such a big topic, the next chapter is all about the wow factor of colour.

Surprise with top to toe colour.

But just before we go there let me just say although it's Surprise that gets you noticed, the other STAR principles, personality, artistry and reinvention, all have to be there as well. Meg's crazy hat matched something adventurous in her personality that she was able to release into the world. She had chosen something artistic as well as unusual (the hat I'm sure was beautiful in some way not like an upside-down hedgehog) and she had, of course, reinvented herself by stepping out of her comfort zone by wearing something unusual but very much in vogue.

But back to colour – a surprise in its own right. This is one of the most important things for style STARS to get right.

Colour is amazing. Its moods, the intensity it brings into our world, and the confidence it can bring. It's the most important single change we can make to give ourselves an instant lift. It can transform us in body and spirit! So here we go with how to do it.

2

Colour

The Exploding Paint Box – Under Control

The best colour in the world is the one that looks good on you.
— Coco Chanel

Life would be so, so dull in a black and white world. There's a kaleidoscope of colour all around us – in plants, trees and sky, on the coast, and in our houses – and we need colour in our clothes to make us come alive. Okay, clashing hues that are glorious in the garden can make us look like out-of-control traffic lights, and grungy greys and dark maroons wipe us out. But the right colours, especially near the face, are a life-changer.

A painter who I was interviewing for a local newspaper many years ago told me that colour made shivers go up and down his spine. 'What on earth was he talking about?' I thought then. Now, after years of working with clothes, I now know exactly what he meant.

And we can use the power of colour to **Surprise**, again and again. Get your colours right, the ones that make you glow and feel confident, and understand the vibes they give out – and this can be the most important thing in making you a style STAR.

If you are in any doubt about the impact of colour, think of the shimmering, multi-tone shades of silk, or flower petals in sunshine. Or when you pointed out a rainbow to a child. That's the sort of intense pleasure my painter was talking about. Imagine that you and everyone else had to wear a sack every day in either black or brown. Then imagine that you could choose the colour of your sack. You could have turquoise, ivory, scarlet, banana, royal blue, navy, peppermint, olive, pistachio, lemon, lilac and as many as you wanted. That wouldn't be half as bad would it?

Most of us appreciate colour, but don't always know how to choose the wow-factor for our own clothes. Even if we think we're savvy, it's easy to get into a rut and choose the shades we liked years ago, when we had peachy skin and could wear anything. And we can be influenced by a partner or friend. 'My husband always likes me in blue' or 'My girlfriend says black washes me out'. We don't have to believe them!

Fashion trends get in the way. Magazines are full of 'the new black' which is brown or navy or beige. And we go for it, blindly. Or the story is green is back, so we choose it and look washed out. When the fashion dictator speaks, we obey.

There are pitfalls in making the right colour choices, but we can learn how to do it. We can find out how to make facial shadows disappear and our skin look fresher, and how to bring a glow to our complexion and get compliments. Can't be bad, can it?

Still sceptical? I can hear you say: 'Well... I do quite enjoy colour. I like looking at autumn leaves. I enjoy picking a new scheme for my living room. But – lighting up my face and looking younger, that sounds a bit far-fetched to me!' Okay. It does sound like rags to riches in one wave of the wand. But read on, and maybe you'll be tempted to experiment, and see what happens.

Listen to Sian Davies from Kemerton, near Tewkesbury who works as a colour image consultant for the *House of Colour*.

Sian Davies, a colour image consultant at the *House of Colour*, runs her own business from Kemerton in Worcestershire.

I was talking to her about the day courses she gives at the studio in her home, when she suddenly stood up, rubbed off her lipstick, took off her fuchsia cardigan and shoes and removed her silver necklace. All that was left was a black skirt and top and she was, in an instant, dull! Her skin looked drab and her bubbly personality disappeared. 'This is what I show my clients. Stripped of colour, I look lifeless,' said Sian. 'The women who come for advice are often in their fifties or early sixties, and some have given up as they get older because they don't know what to do. There are no role models for mature women,' she says. 'The young can get away with anything, although they will always look better in the right colours. But as we get older the most flattering colours can make a huge difference. They can transform the way we look, and the way we feel about ourselves,' Sian adds.

And part of the problem, she adds, 'can be dictatorial daughters, who tell their mothers what they should and shouldn't do. Mum can end up looking too frou-frou, or too frumpy!'

Sian is passionate about women making the most of themselves, and loves helping them find the shades, and combinations of shades, that make them look more dynamic – and younger. 'Colour can be empowering, transformative,' she says, 'because the way we dress affects the way we act, and the way others react to us.' She talked about a time in her life when she felt 'bashed about', and like many other women under stress she became withdrawn and wore dull neutral colours. Then she discovered *House of Colour*, found hues that flattered and energised her, started her own business, and now helps others to reinvent themselves.

One woman, so delighted with her image make-over, asked Sian to help plan her second-time-round wedding outfit, and she, her husband and Sian went on a shopping trip to find a dress for the all-important day. Another client, so delighted with the help she had been given, sent her daughter for a consultation to give her confidence when she was entering a beauty competition.

Sian uses the most recent **Seasons Colour Theory**, which looks at eye colour and complexions to decide whether you are **cool** – Summer and Winter, or **warm** – Spring and Autumn. Then within these categories some women need bright, high-contrast colours (Spring and Winter) and others a softer, more muted look (Summer and Autumn). After a consultation, Sian will recommend a palette of colours which will be the most flattering for each client.

For more information go to the *House of Colour* website (www. houseofcolour.co.uk) which also gives ideas on styling. And if you want to see how the theory really works in action go to the *Kettlewell* website (www.kettlewellcolours.co.uk) which shows this year's latest colours, categorised into seasons, worn by celebrities and models. This gives you lots of ideas on how others, and, more importantly, on how *you* can do it!

Theory is all very well – but not for shopping!

So we ditched theory after school or college. Do we really have to understand a theory of colour when we're out looking for clothes?

I almost gave up on colour theory years ago, when I was considering becoming a colourist to further my career as a clothes retailer, after different consultants gave me contradictory advice. With one I was a fresh spring, the other thought I was a dramatic autumn. And, in reality, I found winter magenta and purple seemed to suit. So I proceeded by trial and error, and with what I fancied.

But I found that when advising clients, I did often use the warm/cool because in general it's a good a first step in getting shades right and creating outfits that maximise our potential.

So Here's The Science

Are you warm or cool? It's nothing to do with whether you rush outside at the first glimpse of sun, or need triple layers in the winter. And it's nothing to do with emotions – dramatic diva or shrinking wallflower.

It's to do with your skin tone. Does it have yellow or blue undertones? A yellow-based skin can be porcelain, sallow, Mediterranean or Asian. A blue undertone produces a fresher, or paler complexion (it also, and this sounds counter-intuitive at first, is found in black skin). Although you don't actually see blue or yellow in your skin (perish the thought!), it's there somewhere, in some proportion.

If you're cool, you'll generally look best in most shades of blue, fuchsia pink, teal, ice blue, raspberry, sea green, navy, purple and white.

If you're warm you're better in true red, tangerine, warm shades of brown, apricot, banana yellow, lime or olive green, turquoise and cream.

How to find out if you're cool or warm

You can probably pick out a favourite colour from those I've just mentioned, so that's the first clue. What you like best tells you whether you're warm or cool. But here are some other ideas.

Ask your friends. Or, better, ask friends who seem to get colours right themselves. Go shopping with them and ask them for their honest opinion when you hold different shades near your face.

They may know about the warm/cool system, or they may be using know-how from many years of shopping. Whatever, they'll get you started on colour appreciation, and what it can do for you.

Another easy way is to hold up gold or silver cloth next to your face. If gold makes you look better, your skin is warm. If silver flatters, yours is a cool complexion. You can use gold and silver jewellery for this test, and this is another clue because you'll probably find you've more of one or the other in your accessories drawer.

And how about this? Look at the shades in your home and garden. Have you chosen a warm or cool palette? And if you're a painter, what hues do you prefer to paint with? The colours we surround ourselves with, the ones we like, usually complement our skin tone, and are the ones we should wear.

A more expensive, but thorough, way is to consult a colourist. Google image/colour consultants, and find one in your area. Consultants have more knowledge now than when I was first exploring the ideas. The consultation will take the best part of a day, will include advice about what to wear, and you'll end up with your own personalised shade swatch to carry around with you. You will know how to start finding your transforming colours.

So far so good. We now have some idea of what we're looking for. Anything in blue, or deep pink, or soft honey beige, or a not too dark navy. Maybe a top in pale turquoise for holiday sunshine, or a tomato-red dress for going out. With new knowledge, and maybe a swatch of colours, in you go to one of your favourite shops. You scan the rails.

But where's your colour? It's nowhere to be seen! Fashion has stepped in – and gone 'warm' when you're 'cool'. The particular shade of tomato you want had never even been a glint in the designer's eye when planning for this year. The shade of ice blue you fancied hasn't been in the style book for years. And emerald green, well forget it.

However, at least you know what you're looking for. And patience will be rewarded – eventually. It may take time to explore new shops or you may even have to wait until next season for a particular colour. But you're older and wiser now, and you know, I hope, that anticipation is the greater part of gratification – or have I just made that up!

The Psychology of Colour

I've always loved colour, often wore bright shades, and as a young, shy person I wore a lot of red. I thought it was just because I liked it. Simple as that. But now I realise there was more to it. When I wore red I felt better, more confident. And the reason, colour has moods and sends out messages. Scientific researchers have studied the effects and impacts of hue on how we feel.

Red radiates confidence, excitement, passion, even danger.

Black shouts, 'I'm elegant, sophisticated', or 'Lets get-down-to-business'. Worn without accessories or ornaments, it can whisper, 'I'm invisible'.

Blue is sensible, a steady hand on the tiller.

Brown is reliable.

Pink is feminine, but **fuchsia** means drama.

Yellow fizzes with cheerfulness.

Mid-green points to safety and approachability.

Turquoise is zingy and fun.

Navy is serious.

Purple is elegant, regal and also dramatic.

White is honest and pure.

Try for yourself. When you go shopping, or open your wardrobe, hold up different colours in front of your face in the mirror, and see if you can get a sense of mood, or emotion. It works for young and old, and is brilliant when you're older and need a little extra tlc.

And now, especially for us grown-ups, is some important news.

Red Alert

Whether in the past you wore, or shunned it, don't ignore it now because it's the big confidence creator. There are so many tones and depths of red that there's at least one shade that will work for you.

Red is the colour of confidence. There is a shade that suits everyone. This is a russet-red dress from *Toast*.

It might be warm fuchsia, tomato red, coral, raspberry or terracotta red, and it doesn't have be the colour of a whole garment. The confidence effect will come from a scarf, bag or shoes. There's a shade that works for all of us young-at-hearters. White hair looks stunning with warm tomato red, steel-grey hair looks best with shades of raspberry, or deep fuchsia.

We don't always have the natural energy of the young, but we can have the revitalising power of red to boost confidence and energy.

Black Beauty

Black, the colour of grief, is a mystery. It's not a colour say the physicists. It absorbs the entire light spectrum. But we *see* it as colour. And it symbolises opposites – death and elegance. As a fashion item you love it, or hate it. Close to the face, and without any other colour or embellishment, it can be sinister. But a well-cut dress in a black fabric which has texture or slight sheen, together with a piece of jewellery or contrast-colour scarf, can look superbly elegant and vibrant. Black does have a place in our wardrobes.

'You just wait and see. You'll come back to black.' This was said to me when I was in my early fifties by a client after I complained I couldn't wear black any more. Now I do wear black. Never unremittingly from top to toe, nor near the face. Never in a dull fabric (be careful of cheap linen and cotton). And never without a scarf or jewellery.

There was a time in the past, and in some places now, when women of a certain age took to sombre colours, often black, as if they were being dismissed from the social scene. Even in our present, youth-obsessed western culture it can often be difficult for mature women to be seen, and have a voice. But things are changing, and black as a fashion aid doesn't need to mean a cloak of invisibility. It can be a show stopper if used carefully.

There are a few of us grown-ups who naturally look good in black – those with black, dark or silver hair, and porcelain or pink-tinged skin. But we can all do it if we're careful with necklines and accessories. Fashion retailer Michelle, owner of *LBD*, a clothes boutique in Stow on the Wold, says: 'Black is the easiest, quickest way to get a chic,

Spice black with lime, or your flattering colour.

contemporary look. Many women think it's draining, but everyone can wear it as long as they choose the right clean-cut neck-line, not too near the face, the right jewellery, or bright or glossy lippy.'

Black is also perfect worn as a single piece of clothing such as trousers, a skirt or a top, because it can be teemed with absolutely any colour you fancy. For a fresh look, add white or off-white to black, or for drama add any shade or red, pink or fuschia, yellow, lime or deep blue. To be elegant or feminine, add pastels.

And as everybody knows – black is slimming. What's not to hate about that.

Your Colour Chart says No – You say Yes

If you love a particular colour, but you really can't make it work, why not wear it on your bottom half, and pair it with a shade that does flatter near your face.

Or pick a bag in your favourite red or pink. Nowadays bags don't need to match shoes, or anything else for that matter. When I was queuing to get on a cruise ship with my husband I noticed a woman in front of me who was carrying a brilliant yellow bag. Against a white top and green trousers, and next to a spotted, yellow scarf, it turned her separates into an outfit. Too much of the shade might not have suited her, but it looked great as part of the total look. I later found out her name was Valerie, and she was travelling with her friend Wendy. Both women had a knack of putting things together to create individual style.

Wear your best colours all through the year

There's no good reason for wearing darker tones in the winter and lighter in the summer, other than the designers seem to think that this should be the case. And what do they know! We've already decided

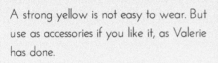
A strong yellow is not easy to wear. But use as accessories if you like it, as Valerie has done.

they don't often know what older women want, so why should we trust them on this. If something suits you, wear it whatever the season. It could be as a main garment or as an accessory.

Three Famous Women

Hillary Clinton wore a white trouser suit when accepting her nomination for president at the 2016 Democratic Convention – giving a message of purity/honesty with a hint at the early twentieth century suffragettes (who sometimes wore white for their public appearances). You might say, 'Well, that certainly didn't work. She lost the presidency'. But colour, though powerful, can't do everything – and certainly not against huge crowds shouting, 'Lock her up'!

Christine Lagarde, French lawyer and politician never varies the short, chic cut of her silver-white hair, and uses colours to complement its stylishness. She wears black, navy and grey, neatly tailored jackets for business authority, often with the addition of a white blouse and nearly always with the skilful twist of a scarf or complexion-flattering jewellery. Off-duty, but still on show, she endulges in pastel pink, brights or white, to add to her silver elegance. She once wore a purple dress with a long jacket in patterned purple and lime. Another time, long white trousers topped with a not quite as long elbow-length jacket – so elegant for the evening.

And I'll not leave out our prime minister, Theresa May. Throughout good and bad times she is always colour and style savvy. She chooses pillar-box red to exude confidence, or to get attention, blue when she wants to radiate calm and efficiency, and black when she's a serious message to give out, or wanted to enhance her authority. And she is cleverly able to wear a wide variety of warm and cool colours, including the softer tones of teal, wine and brown.

Colour is powerful. Its moods, the intensity it brings into our world, its ability to change how we look, and the confidence it can bring. It's probably the most important single thing you can use to give yourself an instant transformation of mood and appearance – and to Surprise. To maximise your wow factor first:

Find out if you're warm or cool. It's not the be all and end all but it's a great start in understanding your best colours.

Look at all the reds and find the shade that makes you feel good.

Don't rule out black. Make sure it's not too near your face, and add bold jewellery, or a coloured scarf.

You can have fun with small pops of colour – in shoes, belts, bags or jewellery – in any colour you like.

Know that there are lots of different beiges. There'll be one for you.

Believe in the psychology of colour. Different colours will change the way you feel, and how others see you.

Know that the right colours *can* transform you.

Next we are going to have a detailed look at accessories – the easy, and not necessarily expensive way to get Surprise into your wardrobe. Remember Meg with her hat? She changed her life. It's always possible!

3

Accessories

The Angel is in the Detail

I can be naked as long as I'm wearing the right pair of shoes.
— Anna Dello Russo, Italian Fashion Journalist

I always remember something a friend said many years ago: 'The pleasure of life is in the detail, in moments which have a special intensity.' In other words the routine of our everyday lives can slip by, day on day, week on week, and year on year. What is important, and stays with us, are the fleeting moments of the extraordinary. Life-changing moments like the birth of a child. The passing of a critical exam. Your first kiss.

But it's not just momentous events that are extraordinary. It's also the tiny details that make each day special. For everyone it's different. Could be the best chips you've ever tasted. Could be a butterfly landing on your hand and resting for several minutes so there's time to take in all its intricate patterns. Could be the sight of the first snowdrops in your garden.

Little things make our personal worlds go round.

And a neuroscientist agrees. In *The Little Book of Ikigai*, Ken Mogi talks about this Japanese concept, which roughly translated means 'purpose in life'. It's all about passion in small things, which for seconds or hours completely absorbs us. Could be our first cup of coffee of the day, holding our new grandchild, walking in the countryside, a weekly session of yoga, emailing an overseas friend. Mogi believes we don't need an overarching, western-style purpose, but we do need to define our small, everyday ikigais.

The angel is in the detail with our clothes, just like ikigais. A piece of jewellery, a scarf, a bag, shoes, we're always being told, make a difference. And so they do. One piece of frivolity, or a beautiful thing – an off-the-shoulder neckline, a gorgeous necklace, intricately patterned tights, a silk scarf of exquisite design, *Liberty*-printed boots (circa 2017), quirky shoes, a finely printed leopard blouse, a sequined something – just one detail added to a simple outfit, can make the ordinary look stylish. And make us grown-up sheep look perky, and show the world we remember what it's like to be a lambs.

Accessories are the details that complete, or transform a look – and be your head-turning **Surprise.**

Caroline, who lives on Guernsey and who travels a lot, has always had an eye for detail. Her latest scarf is a silk, fine-detailed *Ferragamo* square in shades of red and pink and peacock. So, you might think, it's all right if you're rich and can afford Italian couture to make your outfits different. But Caroline has a constant eye for a bargain. She brought down the scarf from €8 to €5 in a flea market in Spain. Her great joy is sourcing clothes from outlet shops, and stalls in small towns where she's skilled at spotting gems from heaps of clothes that you and I would pass by. Caroline's specialty is knowing how to accessorise with a detail that makes the outfit.

'I was a child of the sixties,' she explains. 'I loved experimenting with exciting new clothes and went for various looks, sometimes including false eyelashes, hair pieces, thigh-high patent boots – in

The angel is in the delicate orange earrings worn by Caroline, who teaches dance/exercise in Guernsey.

fact every effort towards achieving a certain, possibly theatrical effect, only too prevalent at the time.'

Janet, an international trade expert, loves a bargain and always chooses well. She's always being asked 'Where did you get that from?' because everything, no matter what she paid for it, looks like a stylish, luxury brand. Topping her list of accessories are necklaces, and her favourite designer is *Eleyne Williams* who creates individual pieces which tell a story. In Janet's collection there's one based on a Georgian shoe buckle with added pearls, another shows dragonflies over a pond.

Shoes complete an outfit. How often are we told, 'Wear this with flats for the day, and heels for later.' And today is the very best time to be flat-footed, or bunion-challenged. Following the success of *Doc Martins*, elegant shoes have followed suit, and you can find lots of pretty shoes now with wider and softer bodies and chunkier heels. Even dressy high heels can be found with soft leather and a wider fit – not everywhere, but by spending a little time searching you will find them.

There are so many brands now that offer comfort as well as good-looks. You can get height, if you need or want it, with masses of choice in wedges, or flatforms or chunky heels. And there are soft shoe-boots, and ankle and calf boots, high and low heeled, that give support and style to us grateful young-at-hearters.

A brand that brilliant for us is *Zaccys*, which makes luxury wedges, of different heights, that make for easy walking or glam occasion standing. They're really comfortable, as well as beautiful, with a high-density memory-foam base and very soft leather. One holiday pair could take you from beach to bar, sightseeing or dinner, and makes your summer dressing foot-hassle-free. They're made in scrummy nudes, metallics and navy and black.

For a more formal look, the kitten heel has come back to give a dressy but walkable option – though not one I would run for a bus in. From *Topshop* to *Tibi* there are kittens heels attached to backless mules, or courts, or strappy sandals, in all colours under the sun.

Slides, designed first for pool-side wear, now come in spangled satin for evenings. These are what we used to call single-strap sandals, but have more substance so they grip better. And goodness knows, if comfort and style were ever needed together, it's for standing endlessly, juggling nibbles and drinks, and edging around the dance floor. If any new-fangled invention shines for us, it's the slide.

My only red line used to be trainers – often described by the fashion pack as the instant youthful pick-me-up for grown-ups – whether plain, patterned or platformed, particularly when worn with dresses or skirts. I thought they were the worst in the mutton dressed as lamb syndrome.

But then one day I saw Janet, the trade consultant who always wears stunning jewellery, in her posh new pink trainers – and my red line became squidgy! Having had polio as a child Janet needs comfortable flats, as, I'm reminded, do many of us who are getting stiff in the joints. And she had discovered a line in sports shoes that were comfortable and pretty.

So now I say bring on the trainers in blue, green, yellow or neon pink if you like them, and they are comfortable... Did I just say that? Any colour as long as its comfortable! Okay. What I *really* meant was go for trainers in any colour that will blend (or clash!) beautifully with your outfit. Let's not get too carried away.

But I still wouldn't take out a mortgage for high-platformed, jewel-encrusted cocktail running shoes that have tottered across many a couture catwalk.

Scarves. The market place is awash with choice. We can change our persona with the twist of a square of silk, or by knotting a chiffon bow. Floral ties add romance and femininity without submerging your body in curtain-like extravaganza. And a touch of animal print, sequin, shine or texture around our necks can give us a funky edge without being overwhelming. Scarves pop up everywhere. In high-street boutiques, posh couture houses, street vendors, markets, museums (exit through shop)… everywhere.

A grey print silk scarf turns a cream mac into an outfit.

Bags are instant style makers. Valerie, pictured earlier, who I met on a cruise ship, has a large collection of inexpensive, but well-designed, colourful leather bags bought in Venice. And this is the thing. You don't have to spend a fortune on big names. There are lots of stylish, good value bags around in shades as vivid or pastel as you like. A large, well-designed carry-all will add glamour, and elegance.

Su, a former restaurant owner, knows how to accessorise. Her multi-coloured bag adds panache.

If you want to splash out on a quality bag, or two, that will last you a lifetime look at the Demellier collection. The brand offers you a one-year guarantee and a lifetime of free repair. Such a good idea. There are clutches, and large shoulder bags with a separate compartment for a laptop/tablet, and most have a removable cross-body strap. The best thing about the ranges is the elegant, pared-down design and great colours you'll never get tired of.

Belts are things of delight. Fat or thin, plaited or plain, buckled or tied, decorated or simple they can add decoration or shape where there was none. Worn on the waist if you have, or almost have one, they make the most of this asset, and for the rest of us they can be low slung on the hips to make your top half look longer, and slimmer. You see amazingly lovely concoctions online or in magazines that you would have to take out a mortgage for, but if you keep your eyes open, attractive, affordable belts are there for the finding.

Glasses. A friend of mine goes to great lengths to avoid spectacles. She thinks eyes should be uncovered and free to reveal the inner you. However, if you've got bags the size of golf balls hanging under your, previously, best feature, I think it's acceptable to cop out of revealing your inner soul. Find several statement pairs of spectacles in shapes that enhance your face shape and in colours that please you which subtly, or unsubtly, hide the shadows. They're a great fashion accessory. As well as disguise, the right shape of glasses can do a brilliant job of making your face look less 'moony', or square, or oblong. It's a great time to be eyesight challenged. Spectacles are a design species of their own. Multiple colours and shapes are there for the grabbing. Be known for your spec collection.

My friend Pauline Daniels, the actor and comedian, has thirty-six pairs of glasses lined up in special cabinet donated by her optician. He knows she's always coming back for more, so he's provided her with plenty of space! Her favourite pair, which cost a fortune thirty years ago have been re-glazed to her new prescription and are still going strong. 'I often dress around my glasses,' says Pauline. 'I pick out a pair I want to wear and choose what will go with them. Just as well, really, my eyesight is so bad if I picked my clothes first, god only knows what a mess I would look like!' Not true actually. She could dress blind-folded and still look good.

Pauline, actor, singer and comedian, has thirty-six pairs of glasses, one for every occasion – on and off stage. By kind permission of Jim Connolly.

Sunglasses, unless you're a celebrity, or pretending to be one, are for keeping the sun out, and shouldn't be overused in the gloom. This really is trying too hard. But when appropriate, they're life savers and can hide a multitude of bulges, spots and dark circles. The round, John Lennon shape, is nearly always in vogue, and suits most faces. Choose small round if you have delicate features or large round if your bone structure is more ample.

Try caramel-tinted day-wear glasses for subtle enhancement.

Perfume. As legend tells it, Cleopatra had the sails of her boat coated with fragrant oils before setting across the ocean to seduce Mark Antony, the idea being that he would get a waft of her arrival even before he caught sight of her. Shakespeare tells it like this:

> 'The barge she sat in, like a burnish'd throne,
> Burn'd on the water; the poop was beaten gold,
> Purple the sails, and so perfumed that
> The winds were lovesick with them…
> … From the barge, a strange invisible perfume hits the Sense…'

The Ancient Eygptians knew about the relaxing and rejuvenating effects of perfumed oils, so you can bet that that Cleopatra would have dabbed it liberally behind her ears, or wherever she thought appropriate, as part of her charm offensive. She knew scent isn't just smell. And you know the story of the only thing Marilyn Monroe wore in bed.

As the twenty-first century perfume designer, Azzi Glasser says, 'Specific odours have the ability to trigger strong emotions, which enhance our behavior and mood… fragrances are one of the most powerful tools one can use to enhance, entice, manipulate and motivate both yourself and those around you.'

This is one accessory we should absolutely put on our Christmas or birthday list.

Jewellery. Like perfume, this has a long pedigree. Shell beads have been found in Africa that are 100,000 years old and the Ancient Egyptians loved jewellery made from gold.

Nowadays, we have gems to adorn almost any part of the body. At a party recently, a slim and very curvy thirty-year-old was happy to display a diamond at the centre of a beautiful butterfly tattoo on her upper (very upper) thigh.

Most of us young oldies, I guess, use gems more conservatively (tell me if I'm wrong!) to pin jackets together, anchor belts, or make decorations for neck, hands, fingers or ankles.

Delicate jewellery is in vogue now, but there are chunkier and funkier designs if you look harder. One London brand, *Nocturne*, uses an unconventional mix of shells, rhinestones, gold-plated brass and marble in its 2017 collection inspired from a visit to Korea.

And there's a shop in Harrogate which overflows with original jewellery both delicate and chunky. India Mahon is designer of the gems, and owner of the shop, and her love of gems started early.

India, when she was four and five, didn't want a teddy bear to take on outings. She wanted to wear extrovert jewellery from her grandmother's collection of earrings, necklaces, tiaras. She wouldn't go out of the door unless adorned with precious gems. Jewellery captivated the little girl. And when she was at home she was also allowed to play with trunkfuls of exotic Indian fabrics – gold embroidered materials, bright silk saris and mirror work quilting with tiny fragment of glass – collected by her grandmother who had lived in India, and her mother who loved the richness of Indian fabrics.

India still loves jewellery, and now designs and makes it for her boutique at 12 Montpellier Street, Harrogate. Sapphires, tourmalines, aquamarines, labradorites, turquoises, amethysts, green peridots sparkle within the jewellery displayed on models and in display cabinets, and on India's work desk in the shop.

All the pieces – necklaces, earrings, bracelets, rings – are a fusion of ethnic Indian and simple contemporary design. Gemstones are central to her designs, often enhanced with silver, gold and rough diamonds. She prefers stones which show their natural elemental markings, and says that soft natural gemstones are more flattering for the older person. As far as possible she uses suppliers who know their sources and how they're processed.

Harrogate jewellery designer, India Mahon, uses a beautiful belt to cinch a monochrome patterned dress.

She also uses eco-friendly horn for her jewellery. It comes from the anckole cattle in Uganda which are farmed for meat and dairy. Previously the horn was burnt, causing a lot of polluting smoke. Now the farmers can sell it for extra income. 'A completely sustainable story', says India.

A cream necklace made from sustainable horn, designed by India.

With an eye to English customers, India recommends earrings made with moonstones, or pearls. 'These gems reflect light, and flatter most English complexions.' The contemporary taste is for delicate jewellery, and India designs many intricate pieces for her clients, but also makes some stronger, statement pieces, using for instance, agate stones.

As well as buying from her boutique, it's also possible to commission individual designs which India will discuss and then make for you, either via the shop or by email (india@indiamahon. com).

Tips

- **To colour-match two accessories looks chic.** Three or more in the same shade looks like you've tried too hard. The age of carefully matching hat, bag, gloves and shoes is over.
- **Everyone can find stylish and comfortable shoes** – even the bunion-challenged. Look for ballerinas, wedges and chunky heeled sandals, boots or shoes made of soft leather.
- **Get a free floating bag liner** to keep your regular bits and pieces in, then it's easy to swap one bag for another.
- **If you've room, it's worth hanging on to all your belts** whatever size, shape or colour because you never know what style will be in next. If you throw one away the next year or two you might regret it.
- **The same goes for scarves.** They don't take up too much room so keep them all, and with the whims of fashion, they might come in as one of your perfect **Surprise** items a bit further down the line.

- **Less is more for begemmed or beaded body adornment.** For most of us, although jewellery has rejuvenating and uplifting effects, it is best to enhance, rather than *be* the outfit

So. Surprise! Wow! You can do it! I hope you are beginning to enjoy your journey to being a STAR. Next are lots of ideas on how to be true to yourself.

TRUE TO YOURSELF

1

Dress to Your Personality

But Who am I?

The key to style is learning who you are...

— Iris Apfel

Although Iris Afpel, the New York fashion icon now in her nineties, says learning who you are can take years, we intend to help you to get there much quicker.

Are we ready to get down to some serious mirror gazing and honest questioning? Has our 'personality' changed over time? If so, how much should we adjust our fashion image? I'm not suggesting deep inward analysis – we may have worn that particular tee shirt in our former lives – but I'm going to point to four personality profiles that we can identify with, and which will guide us in our search for style.

First, ignore magazines. The fashion pack is always trying to force us into a character type or tribe that only the young can carry off. The idea is to find your inner soul and dress to it. Are we 'warriors' needing tightly fitted body-con dresses, or 'feminine romantics' in sweet pea frilly numbers, or 'action girls' who bare midriffs and wear skin-tight Lycra bottoms?

Now I agree we should be projecting our own character, but I say that good style is letting loose *some* of your 'personality' into the world. We might just want to keep some bits to ourselves! And the characters types that are often put on pedestals aren't always appropriate for us of the wise generation.

The first question for us young-at-hearters is how do we know what is our 'inner self'. We do change as we get older, and we don't always know it, or want to believe it. Sometimes we fool ourselves we can do exactly what we did in the past, and dress as we did. We may have been a romantic, always looking good in flowers and frills, or a rock chic in zips and ripped jeans, or a glamour girl who only had to flash her eyes for attention. But are we still? It's no good trying to be sweetly feminine if pastels and frills don't now feel right, or spending money on silks and satins if we can't find an elegant match inside ourselves.

And why continue to buy funky outfits, once our forte, if at heart we now yearn to be modest, or quietly feminine. We've got to feel comfortable in our skin for our style to work. We'll look more authentic, more 'together', if our outside image ties in with our inner self – or, as some blogger put it beautifully, 'if we wear our personality on the outside.'

But, here's the thing. Have we ever only been one personality? We were probably chameleons in our youth, flitting from funky to elegant in the space of a day. Has this changed now we're older? Probably not. We're still many people inside our heads. Today we feel chirpy, flirty and up to the challenge of wearing something a little bit daring. Yesterday we felt the years weighing down on us and wanted to dress down in something quietly elegant, or even nondescript, hiding in a corner and watching the world get on with it.

So why not embrace all the aspects of ourselves (not necessarily in a single day of course, that would be far too energetic!) and dress differently on separate days. We don't have to squash all of our inner soul into one pigeonhole. But! We just need to remember that our personas won't necessarily be those we identified with in our youth.

However, the more 'personalities' you can identify with as you get older, the more fun you can have. Character has never been set in stone and we're still free to bring to life different aspects of ourselves as and when the mood takes us. We can be shape shifters – just as long as we can really feel the part.

Ernest Hemingway's great-granddaughter, Langley Fox, American illustrator and model, says you shouldn't be afraid to take on a character. 'By putting on a black suit or wearing all plaid, I can become a whole other person. Fashion is about playing with life and experiencing things through the way you choose to be perceived.'

Now, while being true to ourselves (or a part of our self) is important, we, in our best years, do have to be careful not to get too carried away. Full-on punk (early Vivienne Westwood) or let-it-all-hang-out relaxed (celebrities who have the money and advisers to make sure they still look beautiful whatever they wear) might not be the best roles to go for. So I have gone for some 'character' hooks that we young-at-hearters can happily hang our hats on.

I'm suggesting four categories most of us can take on with aplomb. Some might appeal to you, others not, so it's okay to single out one or two for exploration but these are my first go-to choices – Sporty, Relaxed Glamour, Funky, and New Classic.

Sporty

Someone, not so long ago, got the idea that active wear, designed for workouts, should be part of every day life. So posh active wear was born. Add to the pot a few more conventional fashion items, like leather jackets, big jumpers, casual jackets and soft trousers, and there you have it – athleisure. And most of it (except for the Lycra sports bras and tights, and true yoga wear) is more pretend active than real sporty – garments styled like they could be fit for competition, but intended for anywhere but the gym. And this mode is perfect for us.

Sally Perkins, who owned and ran two fashion boutiques until recently, in relaxed/sporty style.

Relaxed Glamour

And it's about time we got back to allure. As the general female population is so often told nowadays, 'We're worth it,' let us young-at-hearters believe it too! Say after me, 'We are still glamorous.' However. This doesn't mean corsets, fish-net stockings or body-hugging satin. But it does mean, possibly, getting out of your comfort zone, and believing that you can still do some shimmying and shaking.

Relaxed glamour is all about improvisation. This see-through white mesh jacket by Xenia Design, makes a simple *Peruvian Connection* black cotton dress look special.

Funky

This suits a person who refuses to give up on edgy. Her thirty-year-old soul is still vibrant in her sixty-year-old body even though she now needs a touch of out-of-the-pot glow to make her cheeks shine. She's definitely not a body-piercer, jeans-tearer or collector of extravagant cutaway tops. But she does indulge in clothes of quirky shapes, with contemporary fabrics of texture, geometric pattern and strong, occasionally bright colours.

A *Mama B* stripey oversized tee shirt over a floaty white skirt makes grown up funky.

The New Classic

The emphasis for this is looking a tad 'dressed up'. But, we must emphasise, not rigidly coordinated, as in matching hat, bag and shoes, or being poured into fitted and darted perfection with the relevant 'shape wear'. What it does mean is an up-to-date version of the mid-century look. I won't say ladylike, because we're all women

Andree can do new classic brilliantly. She puts together a long knit cardigan, well-cut trousers and an elegant hat – all in the same muted soft white.

now, but a way of dressing that gives a nod to past graciousness. Silk blouses, some fitted, some loose, some with long pussy bows that can be neatly or casually tied, pencil skirts, long, fine pleated skirts, simple long-sleeved dresses – these are some of the key pieces for this look.

We're going to look at these four categories in more detail now. And going to see just how they fit with our **STAR** principles.

Turn over the page to learn more about sporty.

2

Athleisure

'Sporty' to You and Me

The muscular, athletic type is not representative of the human race...

— Vivienne Westwood

When I read this I felt exonerated from my past sporting failures. I did start to jog at one time in my life, a long, long time ago, and it lasted all of three days.

But although we may not be dawn-joggers it's still good to look as though we could be. So we're running with sporty. Can I hear sharp intakes of breath? Don't worry, let me explain. We're not talking about baggy trainers, shapeless tees or sweaty shell suits (pardon my language), but there's a world of 'athlesiure' out there much too good to be left to the juniors.

This is the latest big trend in the fashion industry, and it won't give us grief. It doesn't have to require any more energy than putting on a pair of trousers and a sporty-looking top. What it means is a delightful, unholy mix of anything that looks as if, in a former incarnation, it could just have come off the sports field or gym or rocky hillside, while having little to do with actual exercise.

Fashion has been, for the last few years, attempting to say that sweaty workouts and client meetings are, for dressing up purposes, one and the same thing. Odd, this. Maybe the fashion industry thinks consumers are taking more exercise, and more employees are doing workouts before the office. Certainly lots of celebrities have been seen striding out to go to their day jobs in leggings or tights, fancy zipped sweatshirt undone just enough to reveal a colourful sports bra. Or maybe, just maybe, designers were just pitching for something new.

So you get models posing in what look like velvet motor cycle trousers, black leather jackets and fringed boots. And you see logoed sweat tops, hoodies, crazy big knits, fancy tee shirts, joggers, leggings and ripped jeans all fighting for attention on the front pages.

But, what on earth has this got to do with us? Leggings, wow, hold on. Tight Lycra around the bum. Undone zips, fringed boots. Hmm!

Okay. Let me explain. We are looking at a softer version of athleisure which will take us from breakfast to supermarket, out to lunch, and for a walk in the woods. The sporty aesthetic has infiltrated mainstream fashion.

So here's what we are talking about. Soft or wide trousers and track pants that are grown up, comfortable and stylish; cashmere and cotton hoodies; sweaters with pockets you can tuck your hands into; sporty all-in-ones (jumpsuits) in any fabric under the sun (inspired by the first boilersuits worn by factory workers) and bomber jackets in knits or silks which don't look at all aggressive. Or anything, actually, with an easy, outdoors feel.

An angular stole, wide trousers and tee shirt - easy sporty.

And sports-inspired dresses and tops. In summer 2017 I found an online brand called *Kitri* (www.kitristudio.com) which had a sell-out dress inspired by the anorak shape. Sounds strange but it was lovely, mid-calf length with three-quarter sleeves, in sky-blue crinkly cotton, and a zip down the front. I'm hoping they repeat in other colours. Then in September they styled a blouse, in candy pink, after the kagool, a boxy jacket of yesteryear, with a wide, stand-up neckline. Very easy and flattering shape.

And for laid-back loafing, there's weekend jersey leisurewear, which gives you soft trousers and tops that don't encourage you to go much further than the sofa, although it looks (vaguely) sporty.

The on-line brand *Me + Em,* (www.meandem.com) ticks all the boxes in the athleisure trend with an elegant/sporty style combined with a high level of quality and fit. This really does go from morning to evening (with a tweak of heels and jewellery). The Autumn 2017 range had a crease-free twill cropped pant, with a flattering sand and white stripe down the sides which could be worn with slouchy top, blouse, cotton hoody, or softly tailored blazer. And in 2018 came a smart black tapered cargo trouser in washable crease-free crepe.

These garments can be for lounging, travelling or evening dressing. Clever that. Clothes that do it all. I never thought I would see it.

And here's another example from the Autumn 2017 range of *Peruvian Connection* (www.peruvianconnection.co.uk) Although most of their outfits can be described as 'elegant artisan', with clothes inspired by the textiles of the Andes, a sporty vibe also creeps in. In 2017 there was a sweatshirt-inspired long tunic in cotton jersey with slouchy funnel neck and roomy kangaroo pockets, teamed with soft velveteen slim jeans. And in 2018 came a soft alpaca, poncho-styled, summer cover-up. Sporty elegance, smart *and* comfortable.

The 'athletic' look has also spread to other brands not previously known for it. Top designer *Amanda Wakeley* (www.amandawakeley.com) in 2017 described her own style as 'understated sports luxe', and said she often looked at sportswear as a design reference or inspiration. She's passionate about comfort, and thinks there's no reason for any of us to wear restrictive clothing.

So – comfortable and contemporary! We should embrace this trend with body and soul, not just because it looks good, and feels good, but because we still aim to be fit, or at least look fit, even though we may be cracking up a bit around the edges.

How do you know if you would suit sporty? If you can answer 'yes' to any of the following, you could be a candidate. Have you ever enjoyed sports as a young person – country rambling will count. Have you ever admired someone of your age in an oversized sweater, or chunky scarf, or jeans and thought – nice on her but I could never! Have you ever wanted a pair of white trainers, but never dared? Have you ever lusted after a cashmere all-in-one to greet the postman in?

The new sports-inspired wear has become a fully fledged member of the casual fashion scene. My friend Jennifer saw this coming, and led the way. In the early seventies she was always looking for something different to wear. But she always felt the cold and wanted to be comfortable. She bought a state-of-the-art ski suit, an all-in-one jumpsuit in silver grey. It was thinly padded and elegant, and she wore it around the house, or to go out in. She looked so good in this new self-styled sportswear garment, I went out and bought one too. Sadly mine was a size 12, which means 10 nowadays because manufacturers keep trying to fool us that we're getting smaller, so it didn't pass the test of time or I'd be wearing it today.

Jo Davies, owner of *BWD*, a clothes boutique in Wilmslow (www. blackwhitedenim.com) has just turned fifty, and is petite and very fit. After a long career in corporate retail management, Jo decided to go it alone and set up *BWD* to reflect her belief that good style is about simplicity of shape without being tight fitting, and keeping your core wardrobe to a few basic colours.

She often goes for a sporty look. She visits the gym regularly, wearing active wear from her shop, adding her own baseball cap. She says, 'My ten-year-old son started to wear my baseball cap. Why are you doing that I asked him. Because you're so cool!' he said. Sports wear has become mainstream fashion, and acknowledged even by pre-teenagers, who, as we know, can be frighteningly fashion conscious!

When I met Jo, she was wearing black and white patterned leggings and matching sports bra, with black lacy sleeveless tee-shirt over the top. Earlier she had been spinning (for non-gym users this means working out on a static bike) and now she was in her boutique helping customers. The same active wear outfit

Jo Davies, owner of *Black White and Denim* in Wilmslow, loves casual. Her look is always individual.

had been comfortable for exercise, and was now being admired by customers in her boutique.

On the rails were coloured and print pants with coordinated tops, some skimpy for the young grown ups among us, and some with midriff coverage for the rest of us. All the active wear is stretchy enough for gym, and, if your body is up to it, can be stylish enough for a little light shopping, possibly covered with a long soft jumper or cashmere something.

In another corner of the shop there's Jo's own brand of black and white, high-quality basics – tees, leggings, vests and tunics that

Jo's black, white and grey basics range – tee shirts, tunics
and lounge pants – can be layered or used alone.

can be layered under pretty tops and tunics for casual street or home wear. And for the chic occasion Jo has a tempting variety of separates and dresses, many of them Danish, all showing her simple, casual approach to style.

She also stocks a great range of grown-up jeans – dark denims in particular – that can be put with anything from skimpy tops to pretty or funky blouses.

For an elegant, sporty vibe follow Jo's advice:

- Keep to simple, gently fitting shapes. This means dresses without frills or complicated panelling, or darts that try to pull you in where your body doesn't want to go.
- Keep fresh monochrome basics in your wardrobe – plain tee shirts, tanks and soft tunics in the same colour (doesn't have to

be black and white, but these are good colours as you get older) to use as layering, or go under jackets.

- Stick to a few basic colours for your whole clothes collection. This makes it easier to have a coordinated wardrobe and to mix and match.
- Always try to be different in some way.

Now, although jeans aren't strictly part of 'athleisure', I'm going to bring them in here because they were originally horse-riding gear, and for me, and I'm sure many others, this is sporty connection enough.

Denims have the casualness of cowboy trousers, and make you look like you can walk mountain tops, or mow a few lawns, even though you've no intention of doing so. And they've become so much part of everyday fashion that they give off the most relaxed of vibes.

Yves Saint Laurent said he wished he had invented blue jeans because they were the most practical, the most relaxed and nonchalant garment you could put on. 'They have expression, modesty, sex appeal, simplicity,' he said.

Although the cut of a well-fitting pair of jeans now has become curvier than its first cattle rounding garment, blue denims instantly signal, 'I may look as if I'm not trying hard, but I know exactly what I'm doing.' In the sixties and seventies they became hot for the young. Now they're respectable for us all. I've known women who say they wear the same jeans for breakfast, grocery shopping, lunch, light gardening and out to dinner. There might be a notional stab at evening formality with the addition of a sparkly necklace, or scarf, but there might not!

There are now masses of brands all as different as chorizo and cheesecake, well cut and suiting different body shapes. Many labels have firm, stretchy versions that smooth out unwanted bits of flesh without you knowing that you're being gently corseted. And many jeans are so beautifully cut and embroidered, we have to say they're elegant.

Jeans stretch across the whole fashion spectrum from the high street to haute couture. Warehouse provides you with contemporary versions for about £60. In 2017, £1,000 or so would have provided you with an Alexander McQueen pair embossed with a humming bird logo.

I remember being shocked, fifteen years ago in Rome, when I saw that the majority of women wore trousers (including jeans). All, however, were expensively tailored, some delicately embellished, and teamed with classic accessories, bags, shoes and a lot of fur. (It was a cold November). I hadn't up to then – perhaps I was slow catching on – associated trousers and jeans with chic dressing.

A company called *Robell* now makes a wide range of jeans and trousers, in a huge selection of colours, which couldn't be better for us tummy/hip-challenged grown ups. Their jeans have lots of (firm) stretch which makes them as comfortable as leggings, and as smart as the best cut jeans. You can find the brand in many shops, including *Little Black Dress* (www.lbdboutique.co.uk) in the Cotswold town of Stow-on-the-Wold.

Listen to the owner, Michelle:

'Our jeans and trousers are having a massive moment just now. They've been popular for ages, but just now they're flying

Michelle, owner of the *LBD* boutique in Stow-on-the-Wold, has jeans to suit all sizes and ages. She often dresses hers up with heels.

out. Our large range of *Robell* is incredibly stylish, flattering… and comfortable. Our customers say their partners ask if they've lost weight when they're wearing them. The range of styles and colours in *Robell* is amazing. Customers often bulk buy when they've found their most flattering style. They're called trousers, but they're like grown-up jeans.

'There's a style of trouser that will suit everyone. We've put a lady in her nineties in jeans. She was delighted and she looked great,' adds Michelle.

As well as in store, *LBD* has an online trouser shop which also sells the iconic *Not Your Daughters Jeans*, and another traditional smart jean called *Michele*. When I ran a clothes shop up to six or seven years ago, I found that jeans sold better than anything, and were loved by all – plump young women whose hips took on a new streamlined life, and young oldies with skinny bottoms who became 'uplifted'.

However. We don't all like the same things. Kirsty Allsop, TV property and interiors guru never wears jeans. She loves dresses. They suit her curvy figure and glamorous persona. And on my shop floor I heard many times customers say how much they hated jeans because they didn't want to look like a man or feel like a badly dressed teenager.

Fair enough. Some of us like them. Some of us don't. Trousers suit some of us and not others. Many of us grown ups feel more feminine in skirts, and it has to be said that denims can look masculine – the square cut, looser ones or those with heavy studs. The deliberately distressed and holey definitely look better on teenagers.

But just consider that contemporary jeans and trousers offer such a range of colour, shape and fabric that they can turn any top into a casual outfit. And they can also be put to use in the evening, with a posher or sparkly top, or patterned scarf and jewellery.

On Jeans

- If your partner says 'no', don't do them. Passions run deep about this. I don't want to be blamed for domestic upheaval.
- Unembellished dark jeans are best for us. For evening, or a special lunch, they'll make a beautiful silk blouse stand out and seem ultra cool. For daytime they will go with anything you like.
- Investigate the *Robell* range of super comfortable pull-on trousers and jeans if your proportions have strayed in waist or bum.

STAR Guidance

Surprise and delight you will, if, never having appeared in public in anything other than a dress, you put on an oversized cashmere jumper with skinny bottoms. Or if you could choose a jersey top and matching trousers in an amazing colour, red or fuchsia pink, for example. Needs to be one of 'your' colours though. Or how about investing in a cashmere hoody to transform your basic dark jeans? An off-white hoody, with dark bottoms would give the wow impact you are looking for.

True to Yourself. Of course, if never a sporty thought has crossed your mind, or you don't feel right without a neat handbag and a good pair of court shoes, it's best avoid the athleisure trend altogether. There are plenty more 'personalities' to go for. You don't have to do them all.

Artistry sits well with sporty. The shapes of the garments you're stuck with, but the colours you can play about with to your heart's content. Imaginative scarves can be added to the more leisure-orientated parts of the trend. For instance, a posh silk scarf can add skilful panache to a simple jumpsuit (I've put a silk animal-print scarf with a pale mauve all-in-one) or a colourful, large shoulder bag can be worn across the body of a simple jersey two-piece. Avoid pearls or delicate concoctions, but loop, or large contemporary earrings, or a simple chain necklace can add artistic panache.

Reinvention. If you can find just one tiny sporty bone that has been dormant hitherto, nourish it and bring it to life. Put on sports-inspired outfit, and try it out on a (supportive) friend, or partner. You could find that this is a character style that you will enjoy.

If this chapter has taken you out of your comfort zone, I'm now going to take you to a place where you can be soothed by a touch of velvet, and a swish of silk. This is the world of relaxed glamour. Yes, we can still do it!

3

Relaxed Glamour

Far from the Hills of Hollywood

Being glamorous is about strength and confidence
                                        – Catherine Zeta-Jones

A touch of drama is great. The richness of a sequined scarf or beautiful swishy silk dress gives us confidence. It reminds us that we're alive. That there's stuff happening. It tells us we're here only once, and that we've got to get on with it.

We of the wise generation still enjoy larger than life romance, intrigue, betrayal and bad guys and gals in film and theatre – and in our lives! So why not bring some drama into our clothes? Just think sparkler, not rocket.

But glamour, as in 'how glamorous she is', has had its day. Marlene Dietrich and Marilyn Monroe sizzled with it, sexily and slinkily. But twenty-first century glamour is less full-on sexy, more quirky, more to do with being original. It's a daytime as well as an evening look, less erotic, more individual.

To check this out I asked my husband, 'Do you know anyone glamorous?' Right enough he look looked puzzled when I mentioned the word. 'Don't you know *anyone* like that?' I persisted. (Honestly, I do remember being called glamorous in the past!) More bemusement. 'Stop digging,' I thought.

Glamour is the name of one of today's top fashion magazines for twenty-first century women (those, anyway, who are unwrinkled and spritely) who want tips on how to look special but not necessarily sexy. It gives advice on what is the latest fad in fashion, and how to wear it. It gives, every month, tips on skincare and make-up – the lipsticks we can't live without and creams that will dissolve any wrinkles before they appear, and instructions about where we should be parting our hair (I'm tempted to say wherever we have hair, but I won't). It's a magazine about the latest edgy 'fashion', not full-on Hollywood-style allure.

But there's a contemporary version of the former glitzy style which hit the catwalks in a big way in 2017, sending vibrations down to high street and independent shops. This goes by the name 'relaxed glamour' or 'casual glamour' – and this is something we grown ups can revel in. It's touchy/feely, as in velvets, silks, shearling or suede, and a little bit sparkly or exotic, as in a sprinkle of sequins, or lace edgings or satin linings. It's anything in cashmere, or a clever viscose that you want to hold close because of its softness, or a long silk dress you love to wear because it swishes when you walk.

Judith having fun in a simple beige evening gown on board *Vivace*.

It can be extravagant, with lots of mixed textures and fabrics, and/or oversized. Think about a loosely cut cashmere sweater over a satin slip dress or trousers, or a silk blouse over velvet jeans, or a jumper over a chiffon skirt. Or it can be a simple evening dress in crushed velvet.

This provides us with a great choice of glitzy evening wear (even though some of our younger friends would step out in cashmere and satin at midday). Okay, age appropriate! That's the first time this has slipped out, but it has to be said we young-at-hearters do have to take our age into account – occasionally!

But relaxed glamour isn't just for the evening, and that's because it is to do with originality as well as allure. There isn't anything to stop us doing some glam in the bright light of day, only remember, here it is again, the 'age appropriate' thing, and keep it down to one piece of frivolity than full-on gloss, as in a sequin scarf rather than top to toe sparkle, or a quirky jumper over plain jeans rather than with equally quirky trousers. Long gone are the days of Sunday best, and party best.

It could also be something in denim which has a few flower motifs, or a bomber-style jacket made of a shiny or patterned fabric. Or a simple shift dress with strategically placed sequins, or a wrap embellished with faux fur or fluffy pom poms. Even a coat that flashes a bright satin lining, or a sweatshirt with lace showing at the cuff. It's edgy with charm that can spruce up our days.

Jewellery, belts, shoes and scarves all add contemporary glamour with a single hit. Anything that sparkles, or shines, or has a fascinating texture adds instant appeal. One of the quickest ways for us to show we're not ready to be put out to pasture is to add one glitzy accessory – to just about anything.

Relaxed glamour can be a combination of touchy-feely fabrics. Here's a chunky cashmere jumper over a silky skirt.

I got into the idea of relaxed glamour when I was very young, so I'm glad it's now part of our grown-up style repertoire. I remember when I was maybe six, or seven, having a play-box of strange and wonderful clothes – dresses like the ones I'd seen in Hollywood movies with delicate patterns, and frilly-sleeved tops, in muted, bright and dark bewitching colours, and masses of scarves in flimsy, colourful silky stuff.

All this mixture of short and long dresses, blouses and skirts, and accessories arrived in big boxes sent by surface mail across the ocean from an aunt who had married an American. I now imagine he was rich and being kind to his poor relatives, because the parcels kept coming. And every one filled me with joy.

The clothes swamped my small body, but that didn't matter. They fitted somehow, and I tottered around in them, wearing my mother's high heels, pretending to be different people, usually glamorous film stars. Or I would turn into a butterfly with the silk scarves twisted around my arms, and floating behind as I rushed around the room.

Many boutiques up and down the country include this style as part of their seasonal repertoire. An independent shop in Esher, opposite Sandown racecourse, *Bernard Boutique* (www.bernardboutique. com) oozes glamour as we now know it. It's always searching for new labels that push the boundaries of originality for brave women who want to be original. Just the place for us young-at-hearters who want to make our hearts even younger. Where once it was a small boutique, it's now tripled in size to accommodate their sixty or so brands, and there's something for all of us. Some designer lines you might have to save up for, but there are many well-priced gems as well. If you don't live in the area, it has a very good transactive website.

Because brands are always being updated, I won't mention too many, but when you visit you'll be sure to find a captivating range to choose from. In autumn 2017 there were long and colourful *Rixo* dresses and blouses; a delicious range of pretty *Chloe* blouses;

Relaxed glamour is themed in Winchcombe's *Lavender Blue* boutique.

unusual knitwear, quirkily designed by *Chinti and Parker*, and funky garments from *MM6 Maison Margiela*. I fell in love with a burgundy frilly blouse by *IRO*. (Who knows if it'll appear disguised as a Christmas present!)

And there's a shop in Winchcombe, a medieval town which hosts its own special historic landmark, Sudeley Castle, which brings the glamorous look to all of its rails. This is *Lavender Blue* (www. lavenderblue.org.uk) on the main road running through the town.

The owner, Hilary, who defines her aesthetic as 'relaxed glamour', was first inspired by the brand *Mint Velvet*, and is now building her own collections which I think are even more relaxed and 'glamorous' than her original inspiration.

Hilary's brands include *Warm & Co cashmere, Wyse, Lavender Blue Cashmere, Latte, Oui, Brax, Vilagallo* (a gorgeous Spanish brand), *Blend* cashmere/merino knitwear, *Toupy* silks, *Decollage*, *Kapre* scarves which are colourful and gorgeous, and a new brand *Foil* from New Zealand.

The shop also stocks more mainstream brands such as *Marble*, *Masai, Sandwich, Part Two, Capri, Eden Rock*, and *Sahara* as well as a range of accessories and handbags. But like any independent fashion retailer, Hilary is always adding to her stock when new exciting brands hit the scene, and is always on the lookout for luxurious dresses and tops in fluid fabrics, cashmere tops and quirky pieces that will give her clients a glamorous edge.

And when I visited the shop, everyone, including customers, agreed that although 'glamour' was hard to pin down, all the clothes in *Lavender Blue* added a touch of extra gloss that made the outfits individual and special. A wonderful boutique to visit.

STAR Guidance

Surprise. To aspire to glamour at an age when former generations would have taken to knitting in a back room, still perplexes some people, men and women. So this is an easy rating to get full marks on. Just one well-placed bit of frippery will get us noticed.

True to Yourself. To give authenticity to the look, we really have to believe that we're not past it. We have to know that, deep inside, we're still thirty years old, with all the attached feelings. And know we're still worth it!

Artistry. I did say we should use some discretion, and not go full crazy glam. So this is where a sense of artistry comes in. The palette is turned down a notch, or two, so that we give off a sophisticated allure.

Reinvention. Yet again, tune into that thirty-year-old feeling. You can't get more reinvented than that.

The new relaxed glamour is a bonus for us grown ups. It gives us a way of showing off in a contemporary way, and gives us permission be alluring – decorously, or should the mood take us, outrageously! We're still fully functioning human beings, not to be bundled up and stored in the attic.

And next, another way to stay alive. Be adventurous… embrace funky.

4

Funky

How to be Craftfully Crazy

When I am an old woman I shall wear purple, with a red hat...

– Jenny Joseph

We're not talking about dying our hair pink or pinning bits of cloth together with safety pins or ripping or zipping our clothes in unlikely places. We are going for funky, not hard-headed punk. What I'm talking about is a style that's forward looking – 'cutting-edge', unusual, imaginative. It's light-hearted, creative and just a little bit crazy. And it's fun, so why leave all this to the young ones?

We might back off from extremes such as silver boots and red animal tights; or fake lime green fur; or a jumpsuit in fuchsia with a large black wolf motif ('funky' images from the internet in 2017).

But we could, and should, join in and have some fun. What we're looking for are clothes with an edge.

Could just be a detail, leopard shoes perhaps. Or maybe a whole garment of a quirky shape or unusual colour combination that hits the surprise button. There could be large bows which have relocated themselves from front to back, big sleeves with flutes or

Funky is cheeky.

ruffles, lots around in 2017 and 2018, quirky shortish dresses too cute to wear on their own but adventurous if put over opaque or patterned tights or trousers. Anything with spots and stripes mixed together, or patterns mixed with plains. Clever layering can be adventurous too, or a jumper that isn't a jumper but a work of art. Even a sweater that's pretending to be a dress.

Unusual or stand-out accessories – clunky or colourful jewellery, beautiful belts, bright shoes, slides, and boots, amazing hats – all count as funky. And these accessories are clever little devices for gearing up a classic dress, or simple top and jeans. I was delighted recently to get a commendation for my bright-red shoelaces, yes, laces! awarded by a passer-by when walking near the Thames.

Get inspired by tucking into any magazine or website that writes about fashion. There will be a lot of stuff that's way out, age inappropriate! But, in the spirit of adventure, take it all in, modify, adapt, and get inspired.

One of the shops I visited when researching this book was *You Boutique* (www.youboutique.co.uk) in Worcester's Friar Street – a great shopping destination, full of individual and different fashion boutiques, coffee houses and restaurants where you can top up with caffeine or snacks to keep you going longer. In *You* is the brand *Alembika* which ticks a lot of adventurous buttons and is perfect for ladies with curves. The Israeli designer, Hagar Alembik, creates artistic looks with textures and mixed colours that give them a distinctive and funky aesthetic. The outfits are very easy to wear, flow beautifully over ample, or not so ample bodies. And in a no fuss, easy to wear way, come complete with no buttons, or zips. Pieces are designed to go together, so layering is done for you.

These wide pants, in an original abstract print, were part of *Alembika's* 2017 range. The yellow jacket is by Yacco Marricard.

Judy, the owner and hands-on manager, is in the shop almost every day to help and advise customers. She likes funky, but also comfortable clothes that suit women of all sizes.

'I like to think that I offer clothes for real women. Sometimes it can be an outfit for work, a special outfit for a celebration, or something quirky and different. I like to think I have something for everyone. I'm always looking for that new brand to add something exciting to the shop. No time to stand still in the fashion business as it's changing all the time. Natural fabrics are particularly being sourced as the discerning shopper is now asking for pure cotton, silk, linen, wool and cashmere, and there are now lots

of new, gorgeous fabrics in stunning colours and forward-looking designs,' she says.

Judy, who is passionate about her business, has a successful website, and has built up a relationship with many of her online customers who regularly email about shapes and styles. She now ships clothes all over the world, including America and Australia.

Another independent company oozing with contemporary and adventurous clothes, is *Blue* (www.bluewomenswcothing.co.uk), which has shops at Cheltenham and Bath. The boutiques are run by mother and daughter team, Suzanne Temple and Chloe Harrison-Temple. Suzanne says they're risk takers when it comes to choosing brands, and try to offer their customers something they can't get anywhere else. 'You have to be unique nowadays, otherwise, what's the point?' she says.

This means the shop is full of many different forward-looking collections, all of which are 'edgy', and plenty are what I would call funky, including *Rundholz* and *Lurdes Bergana*. Have a look at their website and see what I mean. Their brands include *Bitte Kai Rand, Annette Gortz, 120% Lino, Mama B,*

And another mention for Esher's *Bernard Boutique*. Their whole rationale is providing for brave women who want to be original. So the brands you'll find there, whether sporty and casual, or classic and glamorous, are all adventurous and edgy, pushing forward the boundaries of good style.

Accessories transform. *Blue* boutique (Cheltenham and Bath) styled these *B Rosso* coats with boots and sunglasses.

STAR guidance

Surprise. Funky *is* surprising – though at our age we may not want to cause heart attacks, so let's aim off the full Monty. However, with care, and consideration for others, good ratings will be a doddle here. An unusual, even crazy accessory will do the job, as would a striking pattern, or inventive silhouette.

True to Yourself. Those of a more restrained, elegant disposition, especially those who are inclined towards 'the new classic', see next, won't have any inclination to be funky. And why should they? They can be shining stars without relying on the latest in fashion (they will say gimmicks) that the rest of us might be glad to embrace.

Artistry. We must be sure to bring our fine creative judgement into play to make sure our 'funk' is beautiful.

Reinvention. Remember your young spirit of adventure, and you'll have no trouble in doing funky with ease.

And now a softer note. We're going back to our roots. We're remembering that we're women, who sometimes (or always) want to look like, well… women.

5

The New Classic

We are Women after all

I design for the woman who loves being a woman.
    – Diane von Furstenberg

'I turn up to a rehearsal in one of my trouser suits, and they tell me to loosen up,' says Pauline Daniels, actor, singer, comedian. 'But I already am! I'm comfortable, totally relaxed, in matching jacket and trousers. I hate jeans and tee shirts,' she tells them.

Pauline, early sixties, has been in the theatre all her life. She's performed in Shakespeare plays, musicals, her own Shirley Valentine show, and is the star comedian/singer on cruises and in pantomimes.

And this is Pauline's dress style. Classic. Feminine. Whether in rehearsal, out shopping or having fun. But always classic with a contemporary twist. 'I wear trousers suits in bright, modern colours. I love red. And I'll choose fitted dresses with an unusual print, or something elegant in black and white. A bit of glitter too, especially when on stage, or in the evening. Not too frilly, or floaty, but it must be well made so that it stays where it should. There's nothing worse than something that looks good when you stand still, and then slides about when you start to walk or lift your arms. Or, worse, rides up when you get up from a chair!'

Up to now we've been talking about what some would call extreme style – flouncing around in extravagant velvets and silks, or wearing dresses that feature giant spots or an oversized jumper that's really a dress. Or tending towards the androgynous with blue jeans and 'laid-back' tops instead of proper dresses and pretty blouses.

Fair enough. But now it's the turn of women who want to look like women, as we turn to a style that I'm going to call the new classic. It's for all of us who shudder at wide and weird shapes and wild or bold prints. Those who prefer shapes which don't disguise the parts that make us female. And even celebrate the honest curve here and there.

Am I talking about going back to box pleats, and blouses out of strictly standard moulds, with delicately proportioned pussy bows? Or jumpers that have just two fittings, fitted or semi-fitted, and polo or crew necklines? Or suits that only look good if you've the perfect in-and-out figure? No, definitely not! These were part of the formal uniform of the pre-revolutionary sixties.

The new classic takes these ideas, but puts a contemporary edge on them.

Pleats are here, but fine and swingy – and usually mid-calf length, often in jersey fabrics which are soft and swishy. In 2018 there were versions in jazzy patterns, and jolly colour combinations. There are blouses with pussy bows, neat or exuberant, often in silk or silky fabrics, that can be pussily tied, or left to hang giving a floaty, modern vibe.

There are plenty of trouser suits, fitted and boxy, and multitudes of beautiful jumpers to suit everyone – cropped or long, fitted or loose, fine or chunky, pale or vibrant, patterned or plain, with sleeves that are neat at the shoulder, or 'dropped' for a more casual look.

If you love a fitted or semi-fitted, same colour two-piece skirt or trouser suit you may have to compromise. The current vogue isn't for matching top and bottom, but if you go for contrasting colours you'll do better. And many brands offer tops and trousers/skirts separately, which gives flexibility for those of us whose tops and bottoms don't conform to the norm. (For many of us the normal has long since disappeared after childbirth, or middle-aged redistribution, and/or love of too many things that aren't good for us).

Friar Street in Worcester gives us a shop to rejoice in if we love new classic. It's the *Twenty Five Boutique* (www.25boutique.co.uk) owned and run by Becky Sutcliffe.

One of their key brands is *Sarah Pacini*, Italian-produced clothing, which mixes art and design together to create contemporary fashion that brings us grown-up femininity. It uses fine and textured fabrics, lots in monochrome colours, which drape but don't cling (a double blessing when we can't get off that last half stone), and its styles have the simplicity and elegance that's so female. It's a blend of knitwear, and individual pieces that can be mixed together (instant, no effort layering) or worn separately as pieces to combine with things already in your wardrobe.

Becky also stocks *Crea Concept*, which, like *Sarah Pacini*, concentrates on subtle, but individual styling that's elegant and

A *Crea* cream knit top gives a contemporary twist to an edge to edge cardi.

feminine, and uses distinctive designs and texture to make a difference.

You'll also find in *Twenty Five Boutique* lots of *Cocoa Cashmere* jumpers, and statement pieces from *Oui*, who specialise in jumpers, and tee shirts in printed, contemporary floral patterns as well as plain, simply styled tunics and dresses with a touch of edginess. Much of it's classic, but with a subtle new edge. But as with fashion and books, time moves quickly, and things turn over fast in this boutique, as in any independent, so as usual I'm avoiding mentioning too many brands in a particular season.

Look at *Pure Collection* (www.purecollection.com) online and in store, which not only does beautiful cashmere sweaters, neat and contemporary styles, but also excellent tailored jackets, blazers and coats, with a range of smart trousers to go with them. And you'll find the check jackets that you loved to wear years ago, updated with less emphasis on the shoulders, as well as plain navy and black jackets cut not too tightly, to smooth and flatter. Sizes go up to a welcome 24.

Peter Hahn (www.peterhahn.co.uk), a catalogue and online store (with bricks and mortar shops in Europe) describes itself as 'classic with style', another treasure trove for those of us who want to look like women – or at least more feminine than feisty (feisty deep down we might be, but we don't always want to display it in public). The company has lots of dresses in contemporary fabrics with long sleeves as well as short, flattering necklines and plenty of generosity in skirt lengths. There are tailored jackets, and lovely knits, some neat, some exuberant. Blouses are sleekly plain, or with subtle detail, some to be worn in or out, some in silk with pussy bows, and most going up to size 26.

Another online store that's good for feminine grown-ups is *Peruvian Connection* (www.peruvianconnection.co.uk), already mentioned in the chapter on sporty. Their inspiration is from the Andes with many garments in subtle ethnic patterns, but you'll also drool over many of their elegantly plain knits which comfortably skim the body.

The other great thing about *Peruvian* is that the outfits are shown in groups which do the job of coordinating for you, and they feature (rare nowadays) feminine dresses in delicate patterns in cotton or viscose which drape beautifully.

STAR Guidance

Surprise. If you're only ever seen with jeans and dog, then anything remotely feminine, without dog, will score a hit. If you're neat and naturally well-groomed then you'll have to up your game. Don't buy another plain blouse (you love them, and have lots) but go for one with frills up the front, or ruffles on the sleeve. Or maybe one in a colour you've never worn before – a bright jewel shade that will put colour into your cheeks.

True to Yourself. If you've always worn classic, feminine clothes, you just need to work on pepping up your look with a bit of surprise and artistry. But if you've never felt right in flowers, or well-cut blouses, or have never ever bought a dress, this is your challenge of a lifetime. You might need help from a savvy friend, but if you keep it simple and look for an easy-cut jersey, or print dress and shoes or boots with a block, or wedge heel you're be amazed at the new possibilities that will bubble up.

Artistry. There's plenty of scope for artistry within new classic. Look at *See by Chloe* blouses. There're lots of intricately detailed and pretty blouses that will make you look like a picture. Print dresses are in vogue now, with abstract and artisan patterns. See the *Peruvian* or *Pure Collections* online.

Reinvention. Keep up to date with magazines on online sites. Designers are always trying to make classic 'different'.

6

Image
Clothes Tell Tales

When a woman says, 'I've nothing to wear!',
what she really means is, "There's nothing here
for who I'm supposed to be today.'
— *Caitlin Moran*

When we walk into a room we're judged, in seconds, by the way we look. Scientists tell us that we can be summed up in a glance. Whether we've a sense of humour, how smart we are, and what kind of home we live in. Who we are. Posture and facial expressions give a lot away, but a big part of our image comes from what we're wearing, the colours, the fabrics, the balance, how the whole outfit works. This makes up our persona, and we can't escape it. How we look says bucketloads about us. This is probably the best reason for being True to Yourself.

Dressing to character is the biggest part of creating our image – the image we want to create on any particular day. The clothes we wear reflect what's inside (or what we've suggested is inside). An outfit can help change our identity from student to employee, mother to entrepreneur, full-time worker to part-time retiree. Our choice of clothes gives clues to newcomers as to whether we're approachable, bright, stand-offish or artistic. This isn't just 'window dressing'. As we grow older our image becomes even more important because we need all the help we can in showing we're still alive, and a force to be reckoned with!

Would you believe, yes you would, that Caroline is a dance/exercise teacher – and brings fun to all her classes.

By putting together an outfit that says something about us, means we'll never be invisible in the fashion world that glorifies youth.

But also, how we present ourselves can alter the way we *think* about ourselves and go about our work and everyday activities.

Psychologist Dr. Karen Pine in her book *Mind What You Wear* suggests that clothes, as well as influencing the ways others see us, can alter our thought processes. American university tests showed that students wearing white doctors coats performed 'subtly but significantly' better on mental agility than students in 'civvies'. There was no suggestion, of course, that if we all took to wearing white coats we would be brighter!

And Dr. Pine tells of maths ability tests, when half of the men and half of the women wore swimsuits. The women in swimwear performed worse than their colleagues in normal clothes, but the semi-dressed men did not go down in their results. The difference was put down to the women worrying about how their bodies were being judged, using up some of their thinking power.

Putting together what we wear every day is part of our identity. If we're going to an office it might be more functional than dressy, though it'll probably be similar to what others are wearing. Casual jeans and an easy top could be the uniform if we work somewhere arty, or we might choose something edgy if we're working in a dress shop. For going up a ladder or painting windows, it's overalls or stuff that can be thrown into the washing machine at the end of the day. For meeting friends we'll make an extra effort to look our best, probably taking into account what our friends usually wear.

If we want to make an impression at a job interview we think carefully about what to put on. We don't turn up in our gardening clothes (unless the job involves moving tractors or plants about). Going to the theatre, or a special restaurant, we'll probably wear something that doesn't often see the light of day, to show that we can still glam-up.

Our image is a big part of the way we say: 'This is who we are'. It tells others about ourselves, as well as making us feel different. It's ignored at our peril.

There's another big section coming up now, and this is about bringing something beautiful into our style – and into our lives. Let's look at how we can do this.

ARTISTRY

1

Easy on the Eye

Beauty not Bling

Looking at beautiful things is what makes me the happiest.
– Ali MacGraw, American actress, model and author.

I remember my friend, Stephanie, saying that it was aesthetics that drew her into fashion. It was pleasure in the shapes of garments, in the colours and the textures that gave her enjoyment when choosing and wearing clothes. This surely has to be a big part in what we call creative dressing.

Bringing beauty into style is so worthwhile for us young oldies. I'm not talking about layering on extra bling, or airy-fairy ideas of perfection. We are ordinary mortals and live in the here and now. I just mean adorning ourselves with things that are easy on the eye.

We need the transforming power of attractive things on and around us more than youngsters, whose loveliness can shine out from a black sack held together with safety pins. We need a bit of extra help to deflect from our frailer appearances with outfits and accessories that have a touch of artistry.

I know all that stuff about beauty being in the eye of the beholder. But I would bet my hind teeth (if I had all of them!) that most of us could come to an agreement about what's pleasing if push came to shove. When we look at a famous picture we all know, somehow, that it's a masterpiece even though we can't put it into words. Beauty is something most of us can agree on. (I know some of you may not think so, but without getting tangled up in arguments about the meaning of life, the universe and everything, I'm sticking to my case.)

But how, you might ask, can we ordinary folk get to grips with finding artistic, attractive clothes, and easy on the eye bits and pieces to go with them. Where are they, and how do we know them when we see them? We weren't born with an unstoppable talent for dress design, or sold out our first painting exhibition by the age of six (as did Kieron Williamson from Norfolk now in his teens and selling landscapes at £35,000 each).

Colour

But we *do* all have some artistic flair. We may not get prizes like Tracy Emin and Damien Hirst for an unmade bed and a pickled shark. But we do draw a sharp breath of delight when we see trees covered in autumn golds, or glimpse the dazzling colours of a peacock. And think of the flowers and shrubs you've chosen for in your garden, and how much you appreciate the dusty merging shades of fading hydrangeas, or the blue, orange and pink of a bird of paradise flower.

Colour is all around us. We enjoy it. We love certain shades and use them in our gardens and homes. We have an inbuilt aesthetic sense that allows us to appreciate it.

Shape

And then there is shape (form and proportion) which is also a key part of artistry. If you arrange flowers you'll know what I'm talking about. You use twigs and foliage, as well as flowers, to make eye-catching shapes with vases that can be round and fat or tall and thin. Many of us also indulge in rearranging the furniture, or adding a new bit, from time to time. It's all to do with what looks right where, another aspect of our inner artistry. You don't have to be an expert flower arranger or interior designer to know this. We all have some sense of what looks right in a vase of flowers, or in a room.

We are going to explore these two aspects of artistry in more detail now.

2

Be Creative

On with the New
and on with the Old

Try new ways of wearing old clothes...

— Angela Missoni

Many young people are good at creating individual style. They're the trend-setters not followers of fashion. They'll wear boots with shorts in the summer, a man's trilby with a feminine dress, their grandmother's old fur coat over their shoulder and mix extraordinary fabrics and colours together. They'll search charity and nearly new shops for bargains that will add excitement or novelty.

Now, I'm not saying you have to grab your partner's greasy old panama hat from the back of the wardrobe to wear with your new chiffony evening number. Or, heaven forbid, wear shorts, with or without boots, on a summer evening! But. We can be innovative in our own ways. We can mix textures, and unusual garments together, and paint our own picture using our own original colours. And we should root around second-hand and charity shops. I recently found a *Zara* cream curly wool jacket for a knockdown price in *Beetroot* (www.beetrootuk.co.uk), Stow-on-the-Wold's nearly new boutique.

Forward-thinking young people do STAR style automatically. And though we may have to put our little grey cells on overtime, there isn't anything to stop us young-at-hearters being right up there with them. I hope this chapter will inspire you to be creative.

Maximising Colour

Some years ago when I was considering training to be a colour consultant, I read that a famous British designer (if I knew then I would be writing this book I would have made a note of her name) loved orange and blue. Gloriously clashing opposites – one positively hot, the other ice-cold – and, according to the seasons analysis, never to be seen in the same wardrobe. And this made me stop and think. How could she bear to wear both orange and blue? And did she ever wear them together?! Is it that some people can get away with any colour? Or can just anyone throw out the shade chart and still look good?

So I rethought my colour strategy.

Blue and orange together. Well, I never. But I do now!

The 'warm/cool' spectrum is wobbly

Many of us aren't totally warm, or totally cool. When I was told, by different consultants, that I was a dramatic autumn *and* a fresh spring, and from experience knew that some winter colours suited me, I realised that I was ambi-coloured. And if I was, then others could be too. From experimentation, and observation, I found that many of us can drift from warm to cool clothes, from blue to orange, or fuchsia to red. And we can mix cool and warm together by putting pale blue with brown, pink with orange, fuchsia with caramel, either as accents or part of a main outfit. These combinations defy the seasons analysis, but look wonderful together.

Some women, including us grown ups, can get away with anything.

If you're a 'cool' person, you can dress 'warm', or vice versa. You might even find that dressing in your 'wrong' palette is more in tune with your personality. Some blonds have Spanish blood and don't want to be Scandi cool, so like to try vivid jewel tones. Red heads don't have to stick to the navies and blues of the cool palette. Fuchsia can be an exciting extra to their wardrobe. If you're dropping your 'correct' colours, though, it can help to have a good stack of different lipsticks, blushers and hair dye, so you can add some pink to your cheeks if you're sallow, or some golds if you're of a paler complexion. And punky hair streaks, discretely placed, can enhance your new look. A touch of silver/grey/pale fuchsia in amongst the blonde if you want to go cool, or a touch of gold/russet among the grey to add warmth.

Of course, when you're young and beautiful you can get away with any colour. But that's another story. All this is for us of the wise brigade.

Neutral isn't negative

I'm talking about off-white, grey, cream, ivory, navy, brown and beige, yes beige, and also black if is one of your good shades.

Going head to heel with a flattering neutral is especially good for us young-at-hearters. Neutrals aren't boring, they're stylish and easy. No brain power needed to dress in one, or several different shades, of the same neutral – and the result is elegant, slimming, and looks well thought out. Add a pop of contrast colour if you want, and there you go, ready for anything.

Neutral need not be boring. A silver grey cashmere jumpsuit from *Pure Collection*.

- Grey can be warm (if it contains beige) or cool (if it contains some blue), and charcoal mixes well with most other pastels and vibrant colours. So some form of grey will suit everyone.
- Navy suits most English complexions, and can be teemed brilliantly with any shade of pink from powder to zingy fuchsia, or white.
- Brown is a bit more tricky as you get older. In its dark form it can be drab, and definitely does not flatter grey hair. But there're many shades, from blackish-brown through caramel to soft shades of grey beige. And all browns can work with white or cream to give drama.
- White or ivory need sunshine if you're wearing them in the day, or bold jewellery to give accent to them at night. But in small doses, as a blouse, tee shirt, as a background in a pattern, white is great. Be careful, though, because wearing too much white can make you look like a doctor, or as if you're just going to bed.
- Soft white or ivory, which is better than a brilliant white for many of us, sends a welcome glow to the face, as in the flattering effect of pearls. But this colour needs the same cautions as white – not flattering on a dull, grey day, and needs careful accessorising in the evening.
- Beige, in other lives called fawn, taupe, mink, or even donkey, has had a bad press. Dull, dull, dull. But if you choose the right beige, it can be a flattering basic. Remember, warm yellowy beige is camel, which suits many of us, and looks scrummy with soft pink or navy.

And it's worth remembering that any neutral goes with any other. Gone are the days when black with brown should never be seen. This is now considered a chic combination, as is navy teamed with black.

We can all wear any colour

This is splitting hairs a bit, but interesting if you're as captured by the light spectrum as I am.

Consider red. Nowadays we're not limited to the pillar-box red of childhood paint boxes. With the sophistication of modern dyeing techniques, there're many versions of it – sludgy maroon, raspberry, zingy tomato, pale pink and deep terracotta are all different mixes and depths of what we call red. Some of these suit us, others not. Although they're all versions of the same shade, they're mixes of several hues. You can imagine that maroon is red with brown or grey; or raspberry contains varying degrees of blue with red; and pink might be raspberry softened with white.

And the same goes for all the variations of blue, green, yellow, purple and grey – and any other colour for that matter. Variations of shade are so subtle that there's bound to be one version of any colour that we can wear successfully.

For the science, check out the Munsell system, which explains that the same hue, as well as having warm or cool undertones has different amounts of clarity (amount of white in it) and depth (amount of grey or black in it).

New dyeing techniques have brought the full spectrum of the rainbow into our wardrobes. We can delve into racks of clothes and find the duskiest of pink, vibrant fuchsia, ice blue and vivid cobalt, multiple shades of green from olive to apple and pistachio, warm banana and acid yellow, dove and bluey slate-grey, tomato and berry red, pure white and muted pinky oyster – anything we fancy if we look hard enough.

Admittedly it does take a lot of window shopping, and mirror gazing, and advice from genned-up friends to take advantage of all this luscious choice. But if we're adventurous and tenacious we can home-in on great new colours that light up our faces and keep us alive. Boring old farts we need not be. Bright, glowing young spirits we can become.

How to Find Inspiration

Whenever you're out in the countryside, on the coast, or in a city, look around you. There are immediate, startling shades – for instance, the sea in sunlight or a flaming sunset – but there are also amazing softer shades embedded in houses, shops and churches, and especially in the fine details of brick, or stone, or wood, or metal that make up the buildings.

Use the colours around you to inspire your wardrobe. (Shells I found during a holiday on Shelter Island, an hour's drive east of New York, inspired me. They're a mix of soft tangerine, lemon and pearly cream. I recently found a scarf with these combinations and snapped it up).

Look hard at paintings, in galleries or restaurants, or country homes. Take note of the colour combinations in pictures wherever you see them. And think how flattering that would be for a dress or jacket, or how those combinations would work brilliantly in a print that you could wrap yourself in. Translate the colours you see into your own personal style.

Indulge freely in people-watching. Since we're in the business of what to wear, and they say that imitation is the sincerest form of flattery, let's start with the obvious and look at other women. (And men too. They can sometimes be style inspirations!) Look, and learn from other people's artistry. Look at their colours , and how they layer. How they twist their scarves. What they put with what. If you like it, copy it.

Maximising Colour

- Try black and white. I used to believe this colour combination was too harsh and aging, but now I think the combination suits most of us young-at-hearters, providing we don't go for the big zebra look, or overdo the amount of black.

I used to think black and white was too harsh for us young-at-hearters. Now I have changed my mind. Reinvention is good!

Try brilliant white when the sun is out.

- Go head to toe in similar toning shades. Mix up to three tones, keeping the deepest colour to a minimum. Say, silver top and mid-grey skirt or trousers, with a hint of charcoal in your belt or scarf. Or use shades of blue, slate, navy and a touch of cobalt or turquoise. Or berry, plum and a hint of fuchsia.

- Try unusual combinations. Dusty pink and fuschia; banana and peach; pistachio, apple and olive green; rich teal and fuchsia; turquoise and brown; fuchsia and orange; aubergine and apricot.
- If wearing a bright colour, keep the outline and accessories simple. An intense shade is all the styling you need.
- Experiment with brilliant white. Softer whites – oyster, pearl, winter white, are said to be more flattering against older skin. This is true, in part, but I've also found that just plain ordinary bright white does also look good against skin that has seen better days. Like other vivid colours that suit your complexion, it can smooth away shadows.

Maximising Layering

Layering means mixing together – hemlines and textures – and the idea has been around a long time. I can remember in my twenties putting a long-sleeved blouse under a short-sleeved tee shirt. Very modern! But in the last few decades layering has been taken to new heights.

Although it may sound easy – who can fail at piling one thing on top of another? Actually, we can't put anything on top of anything and end up looking half decent, let alone stylish. So here are some how-to ideas.

- Put a sheer top over a vest or tee shirt
- On top of trousers put a loose-ish cropped tee-shirt or jumper over a longer, fitted vest or top using tonal colours (different shades of cream, natural and taupe, or various complementary reds). Or match the vest to the colour your skirt or trousers, say short magenta jumper over a black tee-shirt and trousers. This makes you look taller and slimmer.

Sheer over opaque is
contemporary layering made easy.

- Wear an oversized, plain or textured jumper over a pretty floral or silky dress. And if you find a sleeveless dress you love for its colour or print, you can then still wear it without exposing your arms. It's more original than topping the dress with a jacket or cardigan which may look too contrived, or imply your arms aren't up to scratch.

Try a loose knit, not a traditional cardi or bolero, over a sleeveless dress if you want to cover your arms.

- Or put a dress over trousers – the 2017 trouser look – and add gravitas. We young-at-hearters can make a 'young' dress, maybe shorter than we usually wear, grown up. Above-the-knee tunics or dresses are best with cropped trousers, not too tight or narrow at the bottom. On-the-knee, slim dresses, go with straight trousers, and mid-calf A-line dresses go with bootleg, or softly flared bottoms.

A classic *Oui* coat over *Not Your Daughters* jeans is clever mix of classic and sporty.

- What about wearing a button-through shirt dress over jeans or trousers. This is a contemporary version of wearing a long blouse or tunic open over just about anything.
- Layer different textures, in similar colours, together – a short bobbly knit top over a longer smooth blouse, or a jumper or tweedy jacket over a silk blouse.

- Use a lightweight coat over a tunic or dress, both the same length, over long, wide trousers
- A long-sleeved, shirt collar blouse under a maxi or midi dress, showing a hint of the blouse top and cuffs, takes a summer dress into autumn.
- Layer pieces of different character together. Not maybe as the young do, with short chiffon skirts and heavy wool jumpers, or knee-length socks with short floral dress – but perhaps a pretty patterned vintage blouse over a tee shirt and jeans. Or a feminine blouse under a masculine tailored jacket, and a print summer dress partly covered by a denim jacket.
- And a tailored jacket or coat looks chic and contemporary worn open over jeans or casual trousers.

Look into your wardrobe with new eyes, and see if you can rearrange the order. Ruffled might go over plain, or vice versa. Things bought separately might enjoy cosying up with a new partner. A tweed jacket you've kept because you love the colours, but never wear any more, might just go over your silky new dress. A good-quality tee shirt, one that's thick enough not to cling, could go with a posh skirt or quality trousers, with added costume jewellery.

Once you start to experiment it gets easier and more enjoyable. Creating a new silhouette by using layering and texture is a great way to add pizzaz, and also disguise any generous contours you might rather not have on display. The short over long top blurs the line where your waist is, or was, and easy tunics or dresses over trousers keep hips and thighs out of sight.

✑

STAR guidance

Surprise, **True-to-Yourself**, **Artistry** and **Reinvention** are guaranteed if you can use advanced layering and colour techniques, so persevere...

Now, we women, whether sporty, funky, glamorously relaxed or classicly inclined, need to party from time to time, whether we enjoy it or not! And what an opportunity to bring out our best artistic efforts. So essential help is over the page.

3

Special Occasion Wear
The Gadabout

Fashion should be playful.

— Paloma Picasso

Most of us like to gad occasionally, if only for a big birthday or special holiday. Every so often it's nice to dress up, be playful, and parade around like a peacock. (Sorry ladies, the peahen, smaller and drabber than its male half, isn't a good example.)

And this is a great opportunity for you to go for artistry in a big way. A party is where you can get away with (almost) anything. That is, if you want to. So this is the chance to give vent to all your pent up 'I can't wear this because of my age' frustrations.

But when the 'smart casual' or 'formal' invitations drop on the mat, or infiltrate the inbox, they can cause grief for months.

Smart Casual

This is the mysterious shorthand for what to wear at loads of special occasions. But pretty much any social gathering – from an anniversary dinner celebration, to impromptu fun get-togethers at the lido, and anything in between, can be caught in this net. So the instruction 'smart but casual' gives no help at all.

Valerie, who I met on a cruise ship, is good with smart casual.

So you ask your friends – and are no better off. You're supposed to look dressy, but not too dressy. No jeans, except perhaps if they've sparkly or embossed bits. A bit of body-clinging might be in order, cocktail suaveness even (but you know you don't have the figure for it). There's always the suggestion that you have to be 'well turned out', but not like everybody else. Original, wow! Not exactly a dress code this. Much harder!

Formal

And we young oldies do have to be on formal duty sometimes in 'occasion appropriate' wear – at our own children's weddings, or a Christmas/business/charity ball, or when we've to posh up for formal evenings on cruises, if that's one of our indulgences.

Do we have to fork out for a new full-length glamorous concoction, or can we get away with something we've dredged out from the back of the wardrobe more times than we dare remember? And what would you wear if invited to a big birthday in a castle, as a friend of mine was. The look had to be 'glamorous', but guests should be aware that there would be cobblestones to cross, and draughty areas to navigate, and possibly sit in. Hmm… will my remedial walking sandals be noticed? Or should I look for some diamante trainers? Could I squeeze some thermal underwear under my latest holiday frock?

Whether it's formal or smart casual, some of us take to dressing up like swans to lakes. Two women I remember on a cruise told me they had left their husbands at home, and holidaying this way solely for purpose of dressing up for dinner. What a good idea! Well, not necessarily leaving partners at home, but having an excuse to dress up.

And even if we groan at the very thought of glamming-up, remember it's good for the brain. Working out how to get away from jeans and jumpers, to something alluring gets our little grey cells working, as does anything else that feels like hard work!

So especially, but not exclusively, for the reluctant party goers, we're going to sort out a few of the headaches that go with finding something special to wear.

First off, you don't actually have to play the game. You don't have to spend hours, and probably a lot of money, on special 'occasion wear'. If you're adventurous, or have an inventive friend, you can delve into imaginative day wear, and put together your own party outfit. Our young culture brings lots of sparkle and froth – pretty blouses, satin dresses, long, shimmery skirts and all sorts of things with attached ruffles and sequins that the younger generation wear for a pub outing but we can collar for evening attire.

My friend Isabel refused to buy the conventional dress and jacket for her son's wedding. She went for a silver, lightly padded, oversized anorak, without hat, and wore it over a simple, long day dress. She was a STAR – surprising, true to herself, artistic and reinventive.

I found a second-hand, bright-pink silk jacket, and put it with wide day trousers for a cruise formal night, and on another occasion wore a simple silk blouse, belted, with a swirly, three-tiered skirt in bronze that I had worn before with a tee shirt.

And there're lots of pretty and printed maxi day dresses now that can be jewelled up for smart casual. Something long and simple can be boosted with a silvery shawl, and or extravagant glitter to make

A DIY special-occasion look - mesh black jacket, by *James Lakeland*, over stripey vest and everyday *Post Card* skirt, with silver long necklace makes a party outfit.

a ballgown substitute. If like me your proportions have wavered, or drooped, over time, and you don't want to be clinched in all night, glamming up something soft and easy is a brilliant solution. The formal, or smart casual, police won't chuck you out because you aren't decked out as a Cinderella.

Dress up a patterned day dress with a large stole in a colour to flatter.

If innovation sounds too much like hard work, and you want a quick solution, special occasion collections come into their own. There are independent shops all over the country that cater, in part or exclusively, for the dressy do. One is in Buckden, St. Neots – the

Anne Furbank boutique (www.annefurbank.co.uk). Of the eleven showrooms, those upstairs are devoted to cocktail, mother of the bride, and special occasions. There's *Joseph Ribkoff, John Charles, Condici*, long-standing players in the field, among many other international and new brands, always being expanded to upgrade the styles. Downstairs the rooms are full of contemporary casual fashion, such as *Marc Cain, Riani* and *Marc Aurel.* There's an alterations service, brilliant when we're height- or curves-challenged.

And there's *The Cotswold Frock Shop* in Stow-on-the-Wold, the small, historic Cotswold town where I live (www.thecotswoldfrockshop.co.uk), which has just about everything for any occasion. They're renowned for their bridal dresses, but also stock huge ranges for the bride's mother, and wedding guests who might want formal or casual dresses or two-pieces, and the accessories to go with them.

If you need advice their staff are always happy to help you choose an outfit for a special day, whether it's for a wedding, prom, graduation, a day at the races, or any occasion where you want to look amazing. Value for money with honest advice and old-fashioned service.

Well established in Stow for many years, the shop is owned and managed by Christine who is there to advise clients most days of the week. One of the joys of the job, says Christine, is not only helping young brides look their best on the big day, but also advising older clients who also want to look their best for a second, or third time occasion.

'Many of our clients have wonderful stories to tell including one lady in her seventies who told us how she met her second husband,' says Christine. The woman had been so lonely after her first husband died that she prayed to meet someone else. In the meantime, she decided she wanted to spruce up her house, and booked a painter and decorator. Whilst working in her home he was taken ill. So she put him to bed – and he never left!

And, Christine tells us, 'The oldest bride we styled was ninety-two years old. Her first marriage had been in war time when she wore a tailored suit. This time around she wanted the full white wedding so we were delighted to help her fulfill her dream. We helped her chose a long, white gown, with all the trimmings, and she looked radiant.'

Wherever you live, google special occasion and the name of your town, and you'll find shops and of course online stores that will help.

The first-time wedding is one of the few big formal events where traditional stands still and many young brides choose a flowing ballgown-inspired dress for their special day. But we young-at-hearters passed that milestone many years ago – the weeks and months of worrying (or drooling over) about how much flesh to expose and whether it should be pure white or modest ivory. For us these are distant memories, if ever in our cash-strapped past we had to worry about such things.

However, we still have to do 'smart casual' as a guest at someone else's marriage. And the wedding guest has the worst of all what-to-wear dilemmas. How are we supposed to look 'effortlessly relaxed', and 'creatively individual' while not appearing to have tried too hard, or ending up like a packaged clone? It can feel like a competition, even though we know it shouldn't. So pressure even before we start to shop.

Really! This is just too much when all we want is to look nice, and drop on something in the nearest shop on the first rail by the door that suits us perfectly.

And not only do we have to look casually different, but there's another hurdle to jump, or in many cases, fall over. A modern marriage celebration often goes on from morning till night, so we've to find something that will look right and respectable in the bright light (or rain) of day, be upstanding for toasts, comfortable enough for a long lunch or 'breakfast' not to burst any seams, and be alluring enough for late night dancing… without having squashed in the flabby bits to the point of agony by nightfall.

Do I have the perfect answer? No. But I'll have a good try!

This is what to do. Approach it like the dance of the seven veils, commonly known as the layered approach. Component bits, in descending order, could be a long – preferably shower-proof – dressy mac, *McVerdi* (www.mcverdi.dk) do quality ones, functional but attractive; comfortable 'dressy' wedges – look at *Zaccys of London* (www.zaccys.com) – no hat, unless this is a feature that you know how to 'work', but always a large, classic bag – *Demellier* (www.demellierlondon.com) do a last-a-lifetime range. Under the coat goes a self-colour jacket worn over a long, print skirt and top with a scoop or jazzy neckline, lots of jewellery (under jacket) to be exposed after supper. Then – a silky chiffon or cashmere stole and small evening bag to be pulled out of the large, classic bag to add evening glamour.

There are endless permutations of veils according to whether you want to maximise glamour – maybe ditching the mac for an exotic parasol, and using lots of floaty, plain and print layers. Or using your sense of adventure – maybe an Asian theme using a satin kimono over whatever takes your fancy. Or opting for classic elegance by going for top to toe chic layers in one colour, your most flattering shade of course. Or maintaining your sporty credentials by copying my friend's exotic parka, and put it over a smart jumpsuit, always in vogue.

Tips for dressing up – whatever the occasion

- Consider an evening trouser suit. There're shapes to flatter every shape. This is easy to wear, appealing and sexy if glammed up with a pretty white or coloured blouse, or dangly earrings.
- A tuxedo jacket (with long, masculine tailoring, and satin lapels) in something other than black. I saw one last year by *The Kooples* (www.thekooples.co.uk) in a soft raspberry colour great with black trousers. Could be expensive, but it would never become out of date.
- Look at *Oxfam* online (www.oxfam.org.uk), or visit your nearest nearly new boutique. Throw-outs are becoming more and more exotic, and this is just when you want to save money for a one-off occasion.

Although it's harder to find the right thing for a special occasion in small boutiques (rather than ordering online) because their main aesthetic is usually casual day wear, but if you're determined to do some proper shopping, always to be recommended, it's a question of being patient and researching your local area. There will always be some independents who will fit the bill.

STAR Guidance

Surprise. A bit of craziness, that you would never contemplate in the bright light of normality, is easier to get away with in a party atmosphere. So the addition of a vivid colour, when you always wear pastels, or multi ropes of beads when your style is minimalistic, or a long floral dress when you've never been seen out of jeans and jumper, will get you lots of points.

True to yourself. This is easy too – because you don't have to do it! You can pretend to be anyone. As in surprise, you can dress 'out of character', just a little bit if you're timid (long sequin scarf) or go all out for your alter ego (full on boho, or drama queen) if you're bold. Just for one night, or afternoon, with an extra glass of wine, you may enjoy being the person you hardly knew was there.

Artistry. This is a wonderful time to try colours you've never worn before, or an asymmetric shape that you've only admired on someone else before. If you get it slightly wrong, it won't matter, this is party time.

Reinvention. Nothing more to say. It's all above.

And in this artistry section we must not forget the final glossing of the lily – cosmetic adornment. Turn over the page.

4

Makeup
Has She, Hasn't She?

The most beautiful makeup of a woman is passion.
But cosmetics are easier to buy.

— Yves Saint Laurent

We young-at-hearters definitely shouldn't do full Goth – but makeup can be a welcome part of our armoury. Forget the throw-away lines of celebrities who talk about only needing lip gloss and mascara. I'm talking about the full war-paint of foundation, blusher, concealer, lipstick, eye shadow, brow pencil and highlighters, some or all of which we can use as and when we want to. But while Goths want to look 'made-up' we don't. We use makeup to make us look, well, the same, but better! And since we're in the era of 'natural' makeup this gives us a head, or face, start. There're wide ranges of every-shade-under-the-sun foundations and concealers to enhance our skin without signalling that they're there.

◦◦◦

Cleopatra used makeup, and so can we. Difference is we don't have to rely on lead and burnt almonds, and ground carmine beetles. We've an endless supply of manufactured glosses and tints from the so-called beauty industry that are probably healthier, though that could be debatable.

In this arena, we, and our younger friends, start on a level (cosmetic) playing field. We don't have special needs. There are brands of skin care and makeup that single out us older ones for special attention. They say we need heavier, more penetrating (more expensive?) creams or primers to smooth and moisturise our mature skin, and special foundations and colours to flatter our failing complexions. But I don't go for this. There's now such a range of makeup and skin care products, that we don't need separate (and often more expensive) ranges. And makeup, whether to achieve a natural or a glamorous look does require creative skill.

However, if you've found an expensive cream, or an 'advanced age' cosmetic that suits you (www.lookfabulousforever.com/uk), fair enough. I prefer to experiment with what's generally available, and it's nice to know that, for once, women of all ages can share the same marketplace. We young-at-hearters can play with potions and paints just as creatively as the rest.

This skill is part of your style quest. It can enhance your individual style. You can mix and blend, to get just the right foundation, lipstick or eye colours. You can play around with concealers, and shaders and highlighters to alter the shape of your face, and use colour to make your eyes brighter, or your lips plumper.

You can end up with a 'natural' look that will take years off your age – and no one will know! But if you want to add glamour to your chosen outfit, then a touch of artistry with eyeliner, mascara and a gleam here and there, will not go unnoticed.

Chance Encounters

I like the idea of serendipity – chance happy happenings that you would never have expected. It was one of those incidents that lead to this chapter.

Derek had taken over our cabin one morning on the cruise ship *Oceana*, telling me to go away while he went over his afternoon talk. When Derek is in working mode you don't argue. So off I paced around the deck for two and a half miles. Not too many other walkers around. Just one or two other keep-fitters giving smiles of solidarity. It was both calming and invigorating with wide open sea views and a tangy sea breeze in my face. Suddenly I realised I had forgotten my sunscreen, and my thoughts turned to skincare and makeup, and how these should figure in my book. Then the need for coffee took over and I headed for the nearest coffee bar.

As soon as I sat down, two fellow travellers sat next to me, Jill Camilla Harrison and her husband David. We immediately started to talk, as you do if you're a coffee addict, about the joy of caffeine in the morning. What a gift at the start of the day!

Jill Camilla Harrison,
makeup artist and facialist.

Then, after we had exhausted the topic of coffee, the conversation took a turn of its own, or so it seemed, to skincare and makeup. One of those inexplicable conversational links that just happen sometimes. I said I was writing a style book. Jill said she had been a makeup artist – of celebrities of TV, stage and screen. What a wonderful coincidence. Here, sitting in front of me, was the just the expert I needed for one of my chapters.

So Jill, face painter of stars of the past, and makeup adviser of the present, agreed to help and here's her story which began with a chance meeting in a coffee shop.

'I was always fiercely independent, and at a very early age when my toddler girl friends were tucking dolls into their prams, I was out with my brother throwing and kicking ball,' says Jill.

But, she continues, she was always artistic and decided that being a makeup artist was her real ambition. She trained as a beauty therapist and facialist, and soon found work in the television and film world, a career which she loved. And yes, it was glamorous meeting the stars – but it was not all delicate brush work, and dabbing off perspiration. Her athleticism proved essential for the job.

'A day could be one long endurance test. Filming on location in particular. Work often started at four am and went on till ten at night. And the makeup artist was first on and last off. There were many rivers that had to be waded, knee deep, and I remember once having to climb half way up a mountain. And if you were caught in the rain imagine all those beautifully painted lips and eyes dissolving in front of you only to be redone, over and over again,' Jill says.

She especially enjoyed working on period sets on location or in the studio. For her, it was great fun going to the National Portrait Gallery, and researching in libraries.

And in those days makeup artists had a vast kit. Hers was stored in four tool boxes, like the ones you can get in *B&Q*. 'This was was a great time of my life and I learnt so much. I had my own, very special brushes, and if any disappeared, all hell would break out,' explains Jill.

In the early days they worked mostly with *Max Factor* and *Leichner* pan sticks, which actually are still available today. But then Jill's hero, *Mary Quant,* revolutionised makeup and revved up the colour spectrum and brought out her famous crayons and powers.

'Remember the doe-eyes and false eyelashes of Dusty Springfield. And the psychedelic brights of eyeshadows and black gothic lips!' she says.

What Jill enjoys today, at the age of seventy, is giving makeup and skincare advice. She gives individual makeup and skin care lessons, and also presents to groups. She says that makeup is more important as you get older because it's something that can really make a difference. A clearer, smoother skin, a peach or pink glow, some fine shading to emphasise good bone structure, good soft lip definition and colour, all these things make for a younger look.

But banished are the days of racoon eyes and the luminous lips and cheeks of the sixties and seventies. Makeup should be understated. 'You don't want people to say, "have you changed your makeup?" You want them to say, "you're looking good, or healthier, or fresher." They don't need to know about your skills as a makeup artist!' Jill reminds us.

The aim is to look yourself but better, which contemporary cosmetics are great at achieving. Especially helpful are foundations, blushes, highlighters, and shaders which are produced in creams, powers, crayons and sticks.

But, she adds, you can still do drama. But discretely. Stick to emphasising one feature, eyes or lips, whichever lights up your face best.

As well as makeup, Jill is always stressing the three essentials of good skin care – cleansing, moisturising and protecting. And gives a warning about cleansing tissues, which can block your pores. If you use them you have to make sure you do a thorough cleanse often.

And contrary to what most people think, unless you have very dry skin, you don't have to use a night cream every evening. Experiment, and see what works for you. Sun and air pollution both harm the skin, and there's a wide choice of sun creams and also foundations that contain sun screen. She suggests protection of at least 15 or 30.

An American friend, Jennie, now in her sixties, always a stunning natural blond, keeps her hair long and blond. Why change a winning style?

'Also, as you grow older, it helps to break the rules sometimes. It's an attitude of mind, to do with keeping your own personality. The rules say long hair is for the young to swish and run their hands through. (Although blogs and magazines occasionally now do show models with long grey hair.) But if you've always liked, and suited, long hair, why change? If you like to colour your hair – keep doing it. You don't have to be grey. Grey doesn't look good on everyone.'

Jill also advises experimenting with your hair. A new hair-do is always possible. Don't be afraid to mix lip and eye colours, and even foundations. Many of us don't have 'standard' skin tones, especially as we get older, so blend two together to get a shade that works for you. And if you like orange, red or bright pink lipstick, but want a more subtle effect, use a pearly colour on top of the brights.

Never be swayed by the current look is Jill's opinion. Fashions in makeup are as fickle as with clothes. Nude is in one year. Next, it's bright, or glossy lips. If these looks don't suit you, or you don't like them, don't fall for the hype. Go with your own choices. Being a rebel is such a help in your grown-up years and gives you a head start to looking and feeling good.

'And above all, you don't have to pay top price for cosmetics or sun care products. Cheaper lines can be just as good as the ones you need to take out a mortgage for,' she adds. Here are some of her favourites.

- *M & S* makeup
- *Touche Eclat Yves Saint Laurent* concealer/corrector
- *Bobbi Brown* concealers
- *Benefit* mascara
- *Bare Minerals* makeup
- *Nivea* and *Olay* are good-value skin care products.
- *No 7* serums are excellent

And here are some of her tips of the trade.

- A lip brush helps with definition, and you can also use it to tease out the last bits of a favourite lipstick. A gloss in the middle of your lips will make them look fuller.
- Cotton wool buds will smudge eye shadow to get a soft look underneath the eyes.
- Eyelash curlers work miracles if your lashes are getting thinner.
- Pull faces in front of the mirror. Helps tighten your cheek and jowl muscles.
- Have your eyebrows plucked professionally.
- Learn to feather-on eyebrow pencil or use a brow powder liner. Aim for a soft, natural line.

- Go easy on the powder. A dewy look is more appealing than a too matte finish.
- Powder over cream eye shadow to prevent smudging.
- Use foundation a shade lighter than your skin tone. Darker is aging.
- Keep to a soft shade of blusher and highlighter.
- Don't go for bright eye colours. Soft blues and browns work well together.
- Concealers are big business now, and magic for under-eye shadows, brown spots and blemishes.
- If in doubt, less is always more.

I've never doubted the power of makeup.

It started when I was twenty years old and working as a secretary. One morning I had got up late, and arrived disheveled at the office. Hair uncombed, probably, and certainly no lipstick. My boss looked me up and down and said, 'What's the matter? You look washed out. Where's your lipstick!' Politically incorrect, verging on abusive by today's standards! But nothing of that crossed my mind then, and he did have a point. I was never high up on the lip pouting scale. I was always aware of deficiencies in that area, and the only trick I knew was to take my lipstick right into the corners to try and make my mouth more Mary Quant than little orphan Annie. We didn't have pearly glosses then to give the 'plumped up' look.

And I remember a wonderful, feisty woman who regularly visited my shop, always keeping her age to herself (her daughters were in their fifties when I first knew her). She told me that the first thing she did in the morning was to put her lipstick on. 'Without my lippy,' she said, 'I've no face.' Margaret Chambers was a very attractive, stylish woman and, if you've well-defined lips, you might not at first understand what she meant. But I did. Because that's exactly how I feel. No mouth, no face!

So lips for me are on the agenda for enhancement. To compensate for decline in the all-important smile area, there're many lip liners that do a good job in defining the fading and feathering edges, and keeping lipstick in place. And there're lipsticks, and stains that last, maybe not all day come what may, but just about through a three-course meal. Then there're sticky coloured glosses, with a transparent balm to put on top (*L'Oreal* do a good one) which have excellent staying power. Also look for *Lipcote*, which has been around for a long time, a liquid that goes on top of your lipstick and does a good job of keeping your colour going.

And let's think again about the colour red. Just as an outfit in this bright primary can give us confidence, why not also red lippy. Doesn't have to be pillar-box red. Any shade from poppy to raspberry will do. Even a softened version with a touch of pearl. Apply carefully – and wait for doors to be opened for you. You'll no longer be invisible.

I've always experimented with dabbing on a bit of this, and a bit of that. So now I'm older I'm very grateful for extra cosmetic aids the industry is continually bringing out so that I can carry on with the 'looking myself, but better' struggle.

But I've always thought, along with Jill, that where facial adornment is concerned, less is more. So the current emphasis on looking 'natural' is excellent for us young-at-hearters. We don't want Dusty Springfield doe eyes, or over emphasised Goth lips. But we do want to make our eyes look wider, more intense, or bluer, our lips to look more healthy. And our skin to look smoother and more glowing with the help of a gold shimmer, or highlighter.

A glow is youthful. Now, what have I said! Am I slipping into the culture of 'youth is all that matters'. The skin care factory is always banging on about the need to look 'ten years' younger. Am I being taken in by this? Maybe a bit. And that's irritating. We could all wish to go back in time, but it's no more likely than a tardis arriving at our front door. So we had better get real and know that a glow can maybe take off a few years, but not decades. If you have naturally well plumped up and silky skin you should glory in it. Those of us who are generously proportioned by choice or nature often have the bonus of good skin, and less wrinkles. But even if your skin is only fair-to-middling you can raise it to a glowing asset with a daily massage of oil (extra-virgin olive oil, if you can tolerate the foody smell) is as good as any, and by topping your makeup with a contemporary highlighter or bronzing product.

Along with younger women we can revel in any of the new pastes and potions we fancy, and not forget that our mature model, Cleopatra, did the same in her day. If tales that have come down through the centuries are true, she enriched her skin with baths of asses' milk, and painted her face to look like a goddess. We can ditch the goddess ambition. Leave that to our daughters. But we can experiment freely with the creams and cosmetics that contemporary science gives us – as long as we're not taken in by the beauty hype. We're not going to look, instantly, many years younger. Nor, as Jill says, do we necessarily have to pay top price for serums, or cream our faces every night unless our skin is very dry.

Let's remember that beauty, think Cleopatra again, isn't to do with Barbie doll, or robotic perfection. Perfectly balanced features, as you probably know, actually look weird. Let's be grateful for our individuality, and take advantage of cosmetics to make us look a bit better, *maybe* a few years younger, and proud to be looked at.

We have just one more section to complete our STAR principles. So here we go with the last one – reinvention.

REINVENTION

1

The Wardrobe Edit

Hoard or Sort

Life is continually changing and we have to accept that reinvention plays a part in how we dress.
— Jo Davies, *BWD* boutique

In a way this whole book is about reinvention – how to transform how we were to how we can be. But I'm thinking particularly about what Jo, the owner of the *Black White and Denim* boutique in Wilmslow (www.blackwhitedenim.com) who introduced us to the sporty vibe, said to me about life changing and the need to change ourselves as well. She believes that reinvention must play a part in how we dress.

Designers of fashion are always developing, adapting, and bringing out something new. Being stylish has to take account of this, whether we're young or middle aged, or in our wise years.

None of us can stay in a time warp and continue to wear what once we liked, or which once suited us, if it looks frumpy and out of date. We have to accept that we live in the here and now, and that we need to keep an eye on what is new.

But this doesn't mean we've to be obsessed by the latest trend. Far from it. We should probably ignore most of them. Contemporary over-zipped or scantily cut tops can taunt us to try them on, but we know we shouldn't (or at least not in front of the children). Some of the latest outfits only look right if we hold our breath, or pull in our stomach muscles to within an inch of their lives. Sometimes we persuade ourselves that our knees aren't as knobbly and saggy as they look in the mirror (it's just a bad mirror) so why not go for the newly minted mini dress (in former times called a tunic)?

However, aside of all the stuff that looks tempting but out of our league, there're lots of new and exciting clothes and accessories that can work for us young oldies. Red boots? Why not? Pink puffa coat? We should all have something pink. Sequined shrug? Good to go with anything. Fur-fringed black trousers? If you're tall enough, go for it! Anything with a flouncy sleeve? If it catches your fancy, it'll raise your style credentials.

We may think we know what suits us, and maybe that is right – to a point. But trends are always on the move so we need to keep an open mind to new possibilities of what to wear. There will be lots of new stuff out there that will also suit us. And unless we sometimes give a nod to what's contemporary, we can be in danger of becoming a dinosaur.

By being prepared to edit our wardrobes from time to time, assess if new styles would suit us, and see if one of our new 'personalities' could be encouraged to emerge, we can be seen as

Go with the young trend and buy second hand.
This is a *Zara* fake-fur trimmed jacket – such a
bargain. How could I resist.

trend leaders and not old fogies. Not sure if we should adopt the oft-said rule about throwing out anything we haven't worn for two years. If we are buying carefully we should be able to hang on to some things for years. But this whole wardrobe edit thing does need to be done, with gusto, every so often.

Now, I'm the first to admit all this reinvention takes courage. If we've worn our hair in one way for years, it's daunting to try something new. If we have dared to wear a hat, not having worn one since we got married, or worn trousers for the first time, it can feel like everyone is looking at us. But that's what we want! Or why bother to get out of bed in the morning if no one is going to notice us. We want people to forget thinking about what they are going to cook for dinner, or if they have turned the hairdryer off... and notice how appealing *we* look.

But change, I know, is hard. 'Haven't I had to cope with enough ups and downs already! Just leave me alone, for heaven's sake! I've had too many challenges', I can hear many of you saying.

And, yes, change does need courage. But getting older doesn't necessarily mean getting more timid. Long-held fears can disappear. Helen Walmsley-Johnson tells a story in her book, *The Invisible Woman*, about stage fright which she'd suffered from all her life. Ari Seth Cohen of *Advanced Style* blog had asked her, when she was in her late fifties, to host a Q and A session after a showing of his documentary about groups of outstanding older women.

'... All evening I had a feeling that something was missing and when I stood up with a microphone in my hand (for the first time ever) I realised what it was – there was a total absence of stage fright... It was the most fantastically liberating thing and I've no explanation for it'.

And I remember a remarkable incident at the top of the London Eye. Derek and I had been visiting friends in London and had some time to spare. He said let's pretend to be tourists and go on the London Eye. 'No way!' I thought. I'd never liked heights ever since I had been frog-marched up the Eiffel Tower as a school child.

But Derek can be persuasive. 'It's totally safe. You are completely podded in. You won't feel a thing!'

So, reluctantly, into the pod I went. I was paralysed with fear from the moment it started to rise and could only cling to the inside seat and look at the floor. A friendly pod companion, and my husband, tried to tempt me to my feet. But, eyes down cast, I grimly clung on. Then, as we approached the top I happened to glance up and out of the window, and a minor miracle happened. Just like a bird let out of a cage, I felt free – the fear instantly dissolved, and for the rest of the ride I couldn't get close enough to the outside window to get the best views.

Now, I am very well aware that fear doesn't always, or often even, disappear suddenly like this for no apparent reason. But it *can*, so maybe we should behave as if it will, and keep on doing the things that we find scary. I was reminded of the book *Feel the Fear and Do It Anyway* by Susan Jeffers and looked at a new, shorter version published in 2017. Well worth a read.

Any attempt to change, upgrade, learn new skills all demand a suspension of belief that we're old – as in 'rocking chair/knitting' old. (Not that I've got anything against knitting or rocking chairs. I love them both. Just not at the same time.) The idea that older people, fifties and ever upwards, are beginning to become less able, less fit, less mentally alert, less adventurous, less aspirational is no longer the case. This is what our parents and grandparents believed, but it is no longer true for most mature people.

We look younger than our parents did, we're generally more healthy and active, and our brains aren't irrevocably shrinking at the alarming rate once thought – as long as we keep using them. According to David Eagleman, a neuroscientist who wrote *The Brain*, when we're engaged in routine activities the brain cruises along on autopilot not registering or storing memory, but the more unusual or exciting the situation is, the more intensely the brain takes it in and records it for us to bring back vivid memories later on.

And, while our brain is registering new things, David Eagleman says, we feel time is being stretched. That can't be bad, surely. Great to be able to slow things down sometimes – as our lives seem to pass ever quickly by.

I rest my case for reinvention.

So now we've started our style journey. We have thought about our character, taken in the STAR principles, and are ready to get going.

But, and it's a big 'but', there is one more important thing we have to know. Remember Drearie Dearie in the Ugh! chapter? Where did she go wrong? And how do we get it right!

2

Attitude

The Awkward Brigade?

Age and size are only numbers.
It's the attitude we bring to clothes that makes the difference.
— Donna Karan

What do Cleopatra, Judith, Brigette Trogneux, Diane von Furstenberg, my friend Janet and a ninety-year-old woman who fell outside a dress shop in Cheltenham, have in common? Cleopatra, queen of the ancient Eygptians. Judith, who inspired this book. Brigette Trogneux, wife of the French president, Emmanuel Macron. Von Furstenberg, the fashion designer famed for her icon wrap dress. Janet, a seventy-one-year-old business consultant. And a fashionable young oldie who toppled on her high heels, and fell on a shopping expedition... What else but attitude!

'Hmmm. I'm not sure about that,' I can hear someone saying.

But let me explain. I'm not talking about being sniffy, or bloody-minded or just plain awkward for the sake of it. What I mean is the drive that gets us up in the morning, and motivates us to get out and going. The thing that fires our creative imagination. The spirit that pushes us to be the person we want to be.

Cleopatra – who inspired Shakespeare and was brought to life by Elizabeth Taylor – ruled in the shadow of the pyramids, but her story has stretched over two thousand years. Why? Because, above all, she oozed wit and a positive attitude that urged her to make the most of her looks, and gave her the power to seduce and rule.

Judith, as well as knowing how to put clothes together, has an insatiable curiosity about life. She's a mischievous sense of humour, and views about the world around her. She presents herself with confidence. When my husband and I had dinner with Judith, her husband and two of their friends recently, the conversation fizzed with strong (amicable) exchanges about politics, fashion, writing sci-fi, global warming and of course our food – every bit of it, including mint marshmallows, prepared by the hostess herself.

Brigette Trogneux, or Madame Macron, wife of the French president, wears the same slim leather trousers for leisure wear as first French lady as when she was a school teacher in her thirties. You may not like her style, but it's impeccably French and well-groomed. This is attitude. Only with strong independent spirit would you dress so elegantly in a classroom, or with such casual chic in your sixties.

The seventy-year-old fashion designer, Diane von Furstenberg has stated that attitude is everything. She travels light and says, 'I think the most important thing is to be in a good mood, and enjoy life – wherever you are.'

My friend Janet, early seventies, international trade expert, says she celebrates every day. 'It's important to be busy and enjoy what you're doing. That's what keeps your mind, and you, young. I care how I look every morning, when I put on my makeup and decide what clothes and jewellery to wear.' She loves her job as an export-import training consultant and will go on as long as she can. Up to 100 if possible!

The ninety-year-old who fell in Cheltenham was outside a shop called *Calico*, sadly no longer there. The former owner, Sally Perkins, helped her to her feet and wanted to call an ambulance, but the feisty lady, famous for her high heels, refused to go until she had completed her hair dressing appointment. Now, I do know that some of you will be thinking she was not feisty but just plain foolish. But you have got to admire her spirit!

All these women know what they want, and have the attitude to get it done. They've independent spirits. They refuse to be dumbed down by society. To be made invisible.

Another friend, Jennifer, always a step ahead in style, told me this story about a time when she was in her late fifties. 'I was off to meet a friend I hadn't seen for a long time, and I'd made an effort to look my best. As I crossed the road away from a building site, I heard the sing-song sound of a wolf whistle.' Nothing to do with me she thought. But it sounded again. And, yes, it was aimed at her, and she couldn't help a smile coming to her face. Then she turned round. 'Oh, so sorry madam,' said the builder, staring her full in the face. Jennifer is very resilient and only saw the funny side. 'At least my clothes, and the way I walked, were up to standard!'

Lest you think I am pathetic (who could possibly feel pleased by a *wolf whistle*!) or politically incorrect (are you actually condoning sexual harassment!) let me just say that although we did not necessarily approve of such whistles of appreciation, we didn't necessarily see them as grossly offensive.

I tell this story to explain invisibility. Mature women are seen as past their sell-by date. They don't get admiring glances in the street, or as much attention as when they were young in the marketplace of life! A big claim, but just think about it.

When you're at a party, you find it harder to make your voice heard if there's a young buzz around. And when you sit in a restaurant it can take ages to catch the waiter's eye. (I know that they're, sometimes, trained to avoid eye contact, but older women are last in the queue to get attention.) You won't be singled out for a 'front of house' job if you can no longer botox or filler-out the wrinkles. And older actresses see their roles shrink (unless they've achieved celebrity status, or are at the very top of their profession).

Older women lose out. Our charms, when we were younger, could boost our standing in the world. As we age we can easily get lost in a fog of wrinkles. Not only do we have to fight aging (although the beauty industry and editorials are slightly edging away from the idea of 'defeating' age, in favour of making the most of it) there's still no big move to say we're more than our looks.

And invisibility can start to blank us out as early as fifty. Depends how resilient, or smooth-skinned, we are! But sooner or later we'll notice that we're being herded, gently but firmly towards the back of the social pasture. And this isn't what we want.

Even in a cosmetics and skin care department, where you might think all women are equal, it's the same story. Mature women don't get a look-in. Jill, our makeup expert who you'll meet later, says she watched dozens of older women in a *John Lewis* beauty department walk away because the eyebrow-perfect, glossy-lipped sales consultants couldn't be tempted away from the younger clientele.

I must add a note here for social scientists who might be reading this, and say that this invisibility is not just to do with how faded, and less youthful we might look. It is also to do with a wider division between men and women. For all that legislation that has said for many years that men and women are equal in the jobs and opportunity market, this doesn't play out consistently in the real world. Women, young and old, are still disadvantaged to some extent by lack of representation and status. And are still often seen as of lesser importance.

So, even if we vibrant oldies keep on with the facelifts and fillers, or force uplifting smiles on our faces, we often still have to contend with an atmosphere which tries to dumb us down. However. A big topic – and enough for another book.

But for the moment it's all about attitude. Because this has the power, if we want it to, to lift any kind of invisibility. So, if we have never pushed ourselves forward in the world, or have never had chiselled cheekbones or a winning smile like Mona Lisa, we need not give up hope.

We can show we have ideas and opinions. That we're curious about life and focused. That we make the most of ourselves. In this way we have the chance to impress with charm and wit and knowledge.

What a relief! Our style rating isn't just to do with how we decorate ourselves. It's about our attitude and how we behave, welcome news for us young-at-hearters who can score high on personality when bodily charms don't always want to come out to play.

A positive attitude is so, so important. And if you think I'm setting the attitude bar too high with Cleopatra, a top designer and a president's wife – their genes or wealth may have given them a head start in their feisty attitudes – let me tell you that Janet, who rejoices in every day, had no such advantages. She almost died from polio as a child, but today no one notices her slight limp. All you see is her smile, her slim figure and sparkling style. She's among the most energetic, well-informed and charming people I know.

Janet - always a positive attitude.

Just to give you one example of her tenacity, she has always worked out in the gym to strengthen her upper body, and build up her general fitness. One day a new bit of kit appeared on the exercise floor. It was designed to strengthen the arms, and looked a pretty simple piece of equipment. Janet had a go, did twenty or so presses, and rated it good for purpose. A young man was keen to show off his prowess, and anchored himself to the machine. He struggled to do five presses, broke out into a sweat and gave up. What humilation!

Soon after I had started writing about style for the young-at-heart I was given a book by Ari Seth Cohen, American blogger and author, *Advanced Style*. He's a young photographer, not yet out of his thirties, who is captivated by glamorous over-sixties women who dress as if it were their last day on earth. He picks out the artistic, the colourful, the funky, the supremely elegant women on the streets of world capitals – women who have wrinkles, but aren't afraid to show them, women who haven't forced themselves in the 'ten years younger' mould of fashion plates.

The pictures are remarkable. The women are uniquely intriguing. Their clothes are dazzling, but their spirit shines even brighter. And this is what Cohen shows us – bright, imaginative older women who challenge the world to look at them, and look at them again!

He believes that the key is attitude – the way we stand and carry ourselves through life truly characterises our style. He started his blog, also called *Advanced Style*, as a forum for sharing the style and stories of mature women who, he believes, are often made to feel invisible. He never looked at *Advanced Style* as being a fashion guide, but rather a place 'to share, to inspire, and to celebrate the wisdom, creativity, and freedom that comes with age'.

When I first opened the book as a relatively introverted Englander, I thought this was all too much crazy fashion and over-the-top dressing by seniors who should know better. But as I looked closer, although many of the women looked like they had a university degree in extreme art, many others presented themselves more quietly and elegantly. And it slowly dawned on me that this was stirring and ground-breaking stuff. His stunning photography catapults older women into the contemporary world of fashion. They become brilliantly alive, and are now on the same page as their younger sisters. Surely this isn't to be sniffed at. We grown-ups want to be part of the mainstream of fashion – and life.

We can all be brilliantly alive, and as aspirational now as when we were younger. As the editor of the American magazine *Allure*, Michelle Lee says:

'If there's one inevitability in life, it's that we're getting older. Every minute. Every second… Growing older is a wonderful thing because it means that we get a chance, every day, to live a full, happy life…'

It's our attitude that counts. We have today. And we're going to enjoy it to the full. But we're also going to plan something new for the future, just like we used to. And if you can do all this with a smile, your star rating will go off the scale! If you look like you're enjoying life (even though at that particular moment you're not) you'll charm those around you. Cheerfulness is catching and brings us closer to others. And there's a knock-on effect. If you're pretending to be cheerful, you might end up being happier.

All this talk about smiling and looking cheerful, you may have thought I've forgotten what the book is about. Clothes and accessories, all by themselves, can cheer us up and boost our get-up-and-go attitude, so I'm going to share a few ideas about 'happy' clothes from psychologist Professor Karen Pine:

- A piece of statement jewellery will make you feel special, like wearing a badge of honour.
- Wearing colours from nature – apple green, sky blue or sunshine yellow give us a lift, because they mirror the world of freshness and energy.
- Playful patterns such as polka dots or abstract prints bring back carefree childhood feelings.
- Mismatched items will give a buzz, because our brain enjoys novelty and surprise. Think about a leather or denim jacket over a floaty dress.
- Loose clothing and flat shoes give ease of movement associated with adventure and travel.
- A vintage accessory, or some old but flattering piece of clothing, gives us warm feelings of the past.
- Flowered prints and floaty fabrics connect us to spring and summer and imply health and femininity.
- And any trend that harmonises with who we really are will boost our inner mood.

Sunshine colour and polka dot trousers would cheer even a dull day.

STAR guidance

With a forward-looking attitude you are probably automatically ticking the **Surprise, True to Yourself,** and **Artistry** boxes. But **Reinvention** is where you will get highest grades. You'll have grasped what is new in 'fashion' before it knows itself! You'll be up there with the style forecasters being, gracefully, avant-garde before the rest have caught up. A positive attitude gives you a head start to achieving full STAR rating.

Now we're getting to grips with what style is all about, and the kind of spirit we need to carry it off. And we already know there're many rewards when we get it right.

So how about taking a short break from individual style, and looking at the array of clothes we have to choose from in our towns, cities and online sites. And bringing ourselves up to date with what exactly is out there.

FASHION TODAY

1

Too Much Choice

It's a Riot

I'm constantly stressed about taking the wrong choices in life.
I wish I had been born a peasant in the middle ages.
Tend your field, get married, have kids and die.
No social mobility, no options.

This was a comment on a Californian website study which said that shoppers were overwhelmed and confused if they had to choose between too many products. They were happier when they had to select from a small amount of samples.

Isn't this going against all that we hold dear? Especially with clothes. Choice is brilliant, isn't it? So many tantalising things on display. Just the right thing we're looking for must be there. The more the better.

But according to the American study, not so. Too many options confuse us. While we love having a small variety to pick from, too much on offer puts our brains into overload. We're wired to cope with selecting one thing over another. If we're faced with too much choice, shopping gives us a headache.

How many times have we said to ourselves, 'This is just too much. I can't decide.' Now we know we're not alone. Dithering is normal – it's official!

Imagine an invitation has just arrived. You need something new; you don't know what you want. You set off to town, but you're overwhelmed with choice. Rack upon rack of clothes in all shapes and sizes – in knits, plaids, plains, patterns, in black and white, primary and pastel. Most of it's too young. Panic sets in after the first hour. It's bewildering, time consuming... And exhausting.

But whichever way you look at it, variety is part of our twenty-first century lives. Consumer goods multiply and metamorphose every year, every month and every week! We thought we had the latest phone, the trendiest dress, now we're told they're out of date. New becomes old before we can blink.

So lots of choice can be a curse. But, it can also be a blessing. Providing we know where to look (skip forward to Independent Boutiques if you want to know now!) and what we are looking for (skip back and look again at our True to Yourself section). There is so much 'fashion' out there that there is always something right if you look hard enough.

If we were children in the forties and fifties, we didn't have this problem of choice. We had ration books for meat, butter and cheese. There might have been a black and white tele in the corner with more 'potters wheel' interludes than programmes, and we might have had a Saturday treat at 'The Flicks', but we certainly didn't have bulging wardrobes. There was Sunday Best and Holiday Best, and make-do, or hand-me-down in between.

The mass consumer market hadn't yet appeared, and the clothes revolution was still hiding in the wings waiting for Mary Quant to arrive big time in the sixties with variety and choice unseen before. Quant, best known for the mini skirt, also brought breathtaking originality for young women emerging from rationing and scarcity. She used fabrics with bright checks, abstract geometric patterns and large florals in her straight and A-line short dresses. She made frilly blouses, stripey hose and shiny white and red boots. New kinds of garments filled the shops. Jumpsuits, the first all-in-ones, hot pants, quirky hats, cute headscarves and berets, as well as shorter and shorter mini skirts, very wide-legged trousers and the maxi coat. I remember a long, dark-red, shiny mac that I absolutely lived in at this time.

And this was a time when colour exploded. You could get dresses in bold block primaries inspired by Mondrian abstract paintings, dresses in bright red or yellow or with swirly paisleys in pink and blue, and multi-hued, zig-zag hose. Pastels were also there. Delicate shades of peach, mauve and apricot were seized upon by the shyer and less bold of us.

For us youngsters emerging from post-war austerity this was variety never before imagined. The mass market had begun and we were enchanted with the range of new and exciting shapes and colours in clothes that we could just about afford. We had begun to get a taste for choice.

But as exciting as this was, it was nothing in comparison with the twenty-first century fashion extravaganza. While we can celebrate variety, the sheer volume of it now can give us young-at-hearters a headache – especially when so much of it looks better on a teenager!

And the main thrust of fashion today is casual which not all of us are happy with. Read on…

2

Everything's Casual

A Little Bit Undone

It's just my aesthetic: to want to feel a bit undone,
effortless but not without style.

— Yigal Azrouel, Israeli-American,
New York-based fashion designer.

My husband Derek was working as a consultant for a tech company, and visited one of London's state-of-the-art virtual reality start-ups to demonstrate some software. As always he was smartly dressed in suit and tie for a meeting with possible clients, and he took along his eighteen-year-old son, Dan, to give him a work experience day. Dan helped set up the computer equipment before Derek gave the talk and demonstration. At the end of the talk when my husband invited questions, all eyes in the audience turned to Dan, in his old baggy jeans and casual tee shirt. The first questions were directed at him! He must be the brains behind the technical know-how. Key people in the tech industry didn't turn up in formal suits and well-laundered shirts.

In this techie environment, dressing down was, and still is, expected. If Derek had taken his daughter, in torn skinnies and off-the-shoulder top, I hope the reaction would have been the same.

In the world outside business, rigid dress codes, with a few exceptions, are a thing of the past. Fashion is all about being casual. If you wear a fitted skirt suit and pussy-bow blouse to go to the supermarket, people will think, 'Who does she think she is?' For everyday, it's often jeans or trousers and a simple top (and for a special occasion an upgrade to smart casual, which roughly means posher jeans and slightly fancier top).

For most social occasions now (we'll look at a few exceptions later) there're no special clothes rules. I was taken as a guest to a golf club in the sixties, and was thrown out for wearing smart trousers. No trousers, of any description, were allowed. The humiliation, the outrage! Nowadays we can usually choose what we want to wear, rather than obeying a dress code. We're expected to do our own thing – tastefully and individually.

We've been given control. Phew! Our job is to pick and choose, to innovate and create, and put together our very own thing – in a casual way. Hard enough for the young and adventurous, even worse for us grown-ups who don't have the majority of designers and the fashion press on our side.

But, never fear! This is what we're here for. We will show you how to do it.

I'm travelling again, and talking to shop owners and shoppers. Most aren't tall and slim like Judith, nor are they models, celebrities or fashionistas. They're ordinary people, like you and me, who love clothes.

Let's hear again from Jo Davies of *BWD*. 'Fashion now is all about being effortlessly casual,' she says. And this is where her own passion lies. 'I never feel the urge to dress up,' says Jo. 'Casual is to do with putting things together that look as if they were made for each other, even if they're not from the same brand.'

Jo, *BWD*, wears a favourite black jacket.

The key to Jo's personal style is that she's always, and will always, try to be different. 'I've never wanted to look like anyone else. How you mix things together and the accessories you use, makes your style individual.

'I mostly wear black, or black and white but it's not always self colour. I like neat feminine prints, and also fabrics with geometric emphasis. Usually I wear separates, but sometimes dresses. And of course our denim jeans, which I wear often, are a favourite to go with almost any top.'

When I first mentioned the word casual to my husband, he thought it meant 'scruffy'. For our parents it did mean 'scruffy'. (For those of us who hate modern trends, and would welcome back twin sets and pearls, a good tweed coat, and neatly-fitting skirt suits, it means ... scruffy!)

And casual isn't 'grungy' – you remember some of the murky, shapeless clothes of the eighties and nineties which were nothing to do with mainstream style. Grunge was a reaction against the flashiness, and excess of fashion, and used dark second-hand clothing to make women look more like men.

So what is it? I'll have a go at saying what I think casual means:

- A little bit 'undone', as when sleeves are rolled up, or trousers cuffed, or a few buttons are undone on a shirt to reveal a different colour underneath.
- Offbeat. Imagine different fabrics put together, like a knitted top over a chiffony skirt, or a leather jacket over a summer

'A little bit undone' - sleeves pushed up and jacket worn open.

dress. Or a bomber jacket, not in leather like the fighter pilots' uniform, but in silk.

- Quirky. I'm thinking of odd shapes, like the tulip skirt which fits at the waist and just below the waist, then balloons out; or a trapeze top, which fits at the bust then flares out over the hips. Or an angular wrap to make an interesting cover up.
- Jeans – plain or patterned. Well, they just are IT, and will have a space all of their own in a later chapter.

Jeans and trousers make mainstream. Andree wears floral cut-offs.

Now, although the casual mode of dressing isn't for everybody – some people hate jeans and this 'undoneness' with a passion that goes deeper even than the love of their nearest and dearest poodle – there's one positive aspect of it that for me almost tops everything else.

Casual is comfortable. Clothes don't grip like a vice. They're cut loose, often including the near miracle fibre Lycra. Even tiny amounts of this stretchy wonder component, incorporated into any kind of fabric, bring comfort. A jacket will move with you, allow your arms to semaphore, never endangering the popping of a button. We can sit down in trousers without flinching, or wriggling. And we can breathe easy without being wrenched in by a savage waistband.

Can you even imagine what it must have been like in Victorian times to wrestle your thirty-inch waist down to eighteen with whale bones and strings, especially when you were older and had to cope with extra lumps and bumps? What joy it's now to slip into a dress, unprimed by the steel-like grip of a bodice, and see it gently 'skim' not cling over the body. How reassuring to find a waistband that looks solid, but has a bit of stretch at the back. What a miracle to find a fitted top that doesn't feel like a straightjacket.

Upper- and middle-class Victorian ladies had etiquette problems we couldn't begin to get our heads round. Casual was not a word to cross their lips, certainly not when it came to the clothes they had to wear. As house guests, they had to appear in a velvet or silk costume for breakfast in the dining room, tweeds for luncheon or a shooting party, an elaborate tea-gown for afternoon refreshment, and fancy satins and brocades with the obligatory full display of jewels for evening dinner.

The seminal comfort moment for me came with the introduction of tights. I've now almost forgotten the stress caused by suspender belts, and roll-ons that rolled off, and only remember the joy when tights brought all-in-one-suspension and instant relief from the pokey and unreliable metal snaps that bit into your thighs. Tights were the must-have item in the sixties to go with the ever-shrinking minis.

Some non-stretchy contemporary fabrics also have a natural 'give' because of the way they're weaved. Think of bias binding which is woven cotton used diagonally, and bias-cut dresses that have a slight sideways stretch. The garment label will tell you about the fibre composition and give clues about whether the material will drape with a good shape, or flop unflatteringly. A naturally pliable fabric needs to be of good quality so that its 'give' doesn't become permanent after a few washings. I've got a blouse by *100% Linen* (www.120percentlino.com) which has conventional firm weave at the front and a knitted linen back which makes the top ultra-comfortable, and multiple-wash resistant.

Modern wool knits are so versatile, comfortable and creaseless. Not only does wool have a natural give, but the loose weave gives it extra pliability. It was in the sixties that Sonia Rykiel first took advantage of this with a design skill that took her to the heights of fashion. She produced skinny jumpers, ebullient sweaters and cardigans with stripes and motifs, and some garments with fluffy textures that only wool can achieve.

Knits are so comfortable, creaseless and of infinite variety! This one is by *Humanoid.*

And did you know that it was Rykiel who first designed pullovers with reversed seams? And there was me thinking these were a contemporary designer quirk.

So… you may be thinking, 'Poor old thing. If all she wants is comfort, let her get out her old slippers, and keep out of the way!' However. It's not *just* comfort I'm raving about. It's the fact that nowadays you can get comfort *and* elegance. Someone landing from Mars wouldn't know you're being supported by invisible wings of Lycra. They would just see how good you look. The comfort bit in waists is well hidden in quality clothes. And Lycra'd fabric doesn't look stretchy. It just looks like the linen or cotton or wool that it is.

But Not Everything Goes...

Casual isn't scruffy. It's worth repeating! Frayed or faded jeans from the back of the wardrobe, or baggy joggers and leggings aren't attractive. Sloppiness isn't what we want. Relaxed style does not give licence to pile anything on top of anything. Nor does it mean tee shirts and flip flops, and not much else.

Nor does casual mean cheap. If a fabric is stretchy it's to be as firm and of good quality. It's no good if a wrap dress stays in place when you're standing, carefully holding a drink, but opens up when you sit down. Okay. Maybe this isn't a disaster when you're young and your legs look seamless and boneless, but not if you want to keep some secrets (wobbly bits or veins?) to yourself.

But it does need to take into account the crease factor. If the fabric in your dress is too thin or cheap, stretchy or not, it'll bag and sag if you as much as breathe on it, and some cottons and linens wrinkle like a prune even before you're putting them over your head.

I'm not saying avoid anything that so much as looks a little worn after wearing, that would rule out all linens, and good quality ones are cool and lovely for the summer, but just consider that most of the time we young oldies don't want the pulled through the wheatfield look.

For this reason polyester can be a part of our fashion armoury. Although it used to be the fabric never to be seen dead in – cheap, plasticy and just a bit common – it's now being reclaimed by designers as the new wonder material, akin to washed silk – which hardly creases.

Casual dressing, for us, also needs effort in the grooming department. Cleopatra knew about it. Although her hygiene practices may not have conformed to the best of ours (pure supposition on my part), she did do the best for her body with (allegedly) ass's milk and presented herself immaculately as a goddess when required.

And presentation (sorry!) has to be part of the relaxed, casual look for us young-at-hearters. Photographers often like the artfully disheveled appearance, which, while chic and sexy for the young, doesn't do much for us. Twenties and thirties can get away with sloppy tops that were not meant half falling off, or wildly tussled bed hair, but we need to look as if we've at least had time to button our shirts and pull a comb through our locks. Unkempt hair and untidy clothes make us look older. Not sure why, but a bit of neatness and polish, does actually help our appearance.

Now, there's another trend in today's fashion that deserves a chapter on its own, because there's a lot of it about, and because it suits us of the wise generation very well.

3

Unstructured Design
Fit and Flare

Say what you like about long dresses,
but they cover a multitude of shins.

– Mae West

The clue's not in the name. If your hands didn't have fingers and thumbs they wouldn't be a lot of use, would they? What unstructured actually means in fashion is that it's structured – but in a different way, more flowing and flaring than the fitted, more tailored styles of the past. And it's ultra flattering for those of us with generous curves, or flabby bits that cry out for a bit of privacy. It cleverly shows off some curves and softens others.

Now, you may have remembered I was dead against the 'tent' look. And you may be thinking this fit and flare is no more than a tent by another name. However, forget Boy Scout canvas shelters

A dress with fit and flare.

and think about the eastern pointed variety with elegant curves and tied-back drapes and then you come near the style I am commending. Some designers who are on the side of us young oldies, have refined the shapeless 'cover it all up' tent look and created flowing shapes which flatter the body.

Fashion labels such as:

- *Flax www.flaxdesigns.com*
- *Sahara www.saharalondon.com*
- *Mama b www.mamab.it*

- *Gershon Bram www.gershon-bram.com*
- *Grizas www.grizas.com*
- *Backstage www.backstage.com*
- *Oska www.uk.oska.com*
- and *Elemente Clemente www.elemente-clemente.com*

are good examples of this style. Clever cutting and quality fabrics let the garments – dresses, tunics, tops and coats – touch where they flatter, but brush over parts of the body that we don't want to emphasise. The result – a draped, feminine shape. It suits all ages, and is especially good for us whose figures have generously or marginally expanded in unwanted directions, as well as suiting slim women who can use the unstructured look to be floaty and feminine.

And let's get this out of the way once and for all. Unstructured garments aren't flappy, anonymous tents. They do have an unusual shape but it is flattering. Unstructured design is generous, often with long skirts, or wide trousers, but shapely, and gives wonderful camouflage in an attractive way for us grown ups. If we're slim, this style can also flatter by making us look cutely petite (well, petite at least). Counter-intuitive, I know, but it's true.

For a quirky take on these easy cuts, look for the trapeze line, gently swinging out from underneath the arms with maybe curvy bits which come out at the side or bottom. Or balloon skirts and dresses which bell out at the side or bottom just enough to look appealing but not overpowering. There are bubble trousers which puff out a little towards the bottom and cocoon coats which bell out at the sides, narrowing towards the bottom.

There are other garments, which come into the unstructured category, which are not so floaty, but also give (unwanted) curve cover. I am thinking of jackets or tops that are square cut and boxy, finishing just below the waist – a good shape if this bit of you has seen better times. Or 'blousons', with a drawstring (or slightly gathered) blouse or tunic bottom that makes the garment flounce out above and around your middle.

This loose blouse, with a colourful butterfly design, makes a brilliant cover-up for a waist that has lost some if its charm.

And look for kimono sleeves, not a million miles away from the batwing shape first seen forty or fifty years ago, where the sleeves and the main part are cut in one piece. Then there are flattering wide-cut jersey or fabric tops that finish with a fitted sleeve creating a slimmer line.

All of these easy shapes are good for us, because they don't hold on to the body for dear life. They leave us alone to breathe. And they're feminine. Someone I met recently, who was slim enough to look good in any style, said, 'I never got compliments when I wore tailored suits in my office job. But now when I wear an unstructured top or dress, I get lots of praise.'

There're lots of brands whose signature style is unstructured and you'll find them in independent boutiques throughout the country. But for a start take a look at the *Sahara* and *Grizas* websites, mentioned earlier, then you'll see what I'm talking about.

Michelle, owner of *LBD* in Stow-on-the-Wold (www.lbdboutique. co.uk) whose core customers are forty-five-plus, loves the unstructured Italian brand called *Mama b*, which she says can be worn by grandmother, mother or daughter. Its signature style is simplicity, with quirky outlines which won't date. New pieces, in different colours or with new detail, can be added to your collection season after season. This isn't part of the throw-away economy, it's a signature style which goes on and on. It may not compete with the cheapest of high-street prices, but it's excellent value for money. *Mama b*'s signature fabrics are soft jersey, boucles and boiled wool – all have firm texture and drape and wear well.

Back in the sixties we find the seeds of this unstructured look. It was in the Barbara Hulanickis *Biba* shops and catalogues. Here you would find black nail polish, feather boas, and spangly wellies giving edge and sexiness for the new teenage market, but also flowing and unstructured dresses and separates for those of us who were a bit older. I remember a long flowing apricot skirt, and simple grape-coloured top from her early London shop which I wished I'd locked away in a moth-proof trunk to bring out today. And I can still recall soft jersey jumpsuits which would have looked oh so contemporary today.

The hippie counter-culture of fringes, long, colourful skirts, wide sleeves, boxy jackets and bootleg trousers also gave us glorious unstructure from which we've never recovered. Free and easy shaped boho has weaved its way in and out of fashion right up to the present day.

But a word of warning. An unstructured garment won't successfully live up to its name if it doesn't hold onto its asymmetric or floaty shape, and again it's to do with quality of material and cut. And if an untrimmed edge, popular with some top designers, becomes a riot of unravelling when washed, then unstructured ends up scruffy.

I found two shops in particular which will delight with large ranges of colourful, contemporary easy-fit clothes.

One you will find in the centuries-old town of Burford, Oxfordshire, where its high street is fringed with buildings that rise and fall in higgledy-piggledy directions, proudly showing their pedigree from the Middle Ages to the reign of Victoria. This is the *Maggie White* shop (www.maggiewhite.com).

The other shop bursting with wonderful ranges of unstructured outfits is called *Loose Ends* in Lymington (www.looseendslymington.com) on the south coast of England. Another small town, like Burford, which has added a vibrant mix of contemporary shops to enhance its old-world charm.

Now it's time to get down to practical advice.

- Because unstructured designs are particularly good for those with generous proportions here are some general tips to look taller and slimmer. You probably know most of these, but scan through and you might find something new you haven't thought of.
- Select clothing in a plain colour, or fabric that has a softly swirling or abstract pattern. A bold geometric design, especially in brights or black and white can widen you.
- If you like horizontal stripes, go for 'variegated' ones with squidgy outlines and different width stripes. It's a myth that all across stripes are fattening.
- Avoid ruffles – any kind of ruffles.
- Long (hip- or knee-length) cardis are good to elongate, and slim down your shape.
- Go to town on big and chunky accessories, bright and colourful if you like. This goes for shoes, bags, jewellery and belts.
- It's worth spending time looking for, and possibly handing out more money, on undergarments as boring as that sounds.

There're so many shapes and sizes to target all, or certain challenging bits of your body, and lots of information about this out there, so I'm encouraging you to do your own research. M & S still do very good ranges at good prices.

- Dress from head to toe in one colour – doesn't have to be black or navy to get the slimming effect. Or choose different tones of the same hue, which also minimises and is elegant. Be careful with white or very light, because this can highlight and expand your outline depending on the drapability of the fabric.

- Show off the top half of you. A pretty (teardrop or sweetheart) or low-scoop neckline, with attractive jewellery, will catch the eye. And you must have heard that a v-neck is good for a big bust. With an interesting neckline you don't need a detailed or voluminous top.

- Smooth not bulky fabrics are best. And choose good quality fabric. This drapes and shapes better.

- Layering is lovely, but don't overdo it. Short top, over tunic, over trousers is the maximum. More than three tiers will widen you.

- Very short skirts are a no-no. Just below the knee or on the calf or ankle makes you look taller.

- Three-quarter sleeves make your legs look longer. Don't know why. And I do know it sounds strange. But I've been pushing up long sleeves for years without knowing why, and it works. Try it.

- Darker colours undoubtedly have a dramatic slimming effect, but you can add bright or light accents to counteract any dullness.

Now, there's a way of dressing which many of us aspire to, but few achieve. And although the name might not quite fit, I'm going to call it 'designer classic'. What I'm getting at is what celebrities and royalty wear, when they're going about their everyday (rather than red carpet) business.

4

Designer Classic

Royal Chic Critique

Celebrity culture is an aspirational culture
regardless of how much you don't want it to be.
    — Paloma Faith, English singer, songwriter

When I was thinking about this book on style for grown ups I asked a male friend where he thought I should start. 'The Queen', he said. Not quite what I had in mind!

But, on second thoughts, maybe he was on to something.

She has a style which suits her, and which she sticks to. She's not afraid of colour. Now in her nineties, still wears every colour under the sun. You could say she has most of our STAR qualities. She surprises with colour, and is absolutely true to her self, her royal self. Her outfits are artistically pleasing. Reinvention? Well, that could be a problem. Being the queen means sticking to the tried and tested, needing to show stability at all times. So she's let off that one.

But other members of the royal family, and celebrities, who can afford couture clothes, or order made-to-measure outfits from exclusive designers, are pushed into the limelight by the media to tantalise us poor cousins. They do look good, whatever age they are, but at what price! If you trawl fashion pages and blogs – just for the pleasure of what we might do if we had the time, money or inclination – you'll see wonderfully covetable clothes that would drain our life savings with a click of the mouse.

If only we had an open-ended budget there would be no more sweat and toil trying on clothes that don't suit or fit – or later fall to pieces after the first wash. We would fill our wardrobe with beautifully tailored, softly draped designer pieces, in delightful palettes not seen on the high street. Clothes that would that make us walk like a VIP.

Designer classic is a mode of dressing that we of the wise generation would love to adopt – if only we had the money!

Gillian Wolfe CBE, aged seventy, Learning, Arts & Heritage Consultant, who takes pleasure in being well-dressed, talks about the need for the fashion industry to provide more age-appropriate and stylish outfits – *at affordable prices.*

'High end fashion has a more subtle colour range than the few shades prescribed each year by high-street fashion designers – but at a cost. Quality makes are now crazy prices beyond the reach of most of the population,' says Gillian. How many of us can spend £1000 on a single item, she asks. And yet this is shown as apparently normal in fashion writing.

'We see media stars and royalty in gorgeous clothes, mostly made to measure or outrageously expensive designer wear. The stylish woman on a restricted budget has little chance of finding such beautifully tailored clothes, well-fitting with individuality,' she adds.

Gillian voices many of the complaints we young-at-hearters make about our contemporary, young-focused fashion industry by suggesting that sleeveless dresses do not flatter the older woman. The coy solution of a cardigan, shrug or jacket to cover the arms spoils the line of a well-cut dress though is a clever way to sell two items rather than one, she suggests. And when we do see dresses with sleeves, the hem is often ludicrously short and revealing.

'Wrap-around dresses show an expanse of décolleté that best suits smooth young skin. Interesting neckline shapes and collars work well for older women but have virtually disappeared from dresses and woolens except in retro clothes. These require more skill to produce but make for more individual and stylish clothes,' she says.

Gillian also voices a concern about the quality of contemporary fabrics. The material may be a low-thread count and too thin, like many chain-store cashmeres that soon lose shape or silk that creases when you look at it. Clothes need to pass the crease test because who has time for constant pressing. And she points out that fashion dictates just one or two 'in' colours each season. Apart from these, the rest is largely a landscape of safe black, dull navy and smart grey. 'A friend once remarked that a particular chain of fashion looked like a funeral outfitters,' she adds.

She is also critical of occasion wear, much of it being sleeveless and strappy, and says suitable evening wear is a rarity. A stylish dinner dress is the Holy Grail – rarely, or never to be found. Smart casual is also difficult, and again, cut, finish and colour is available only at a cost.

*

Gillian isn't alone in finding the current fashion scene lacking in classic, quality clothes which don't cost a fortune. And forget the so-called 'classic' line *M & S* brought out a few years ago which bombed because it was in no way appealing or classy. It was just plain frumpy.

What we want is simplicity of design, good tailoring, trouser and skirt suits, tops and dresses with sleeves, and coordinated pieces that give elegant streamlining. We want a range of colours, not just black and navy or too-vivid fuchsia and cobalt blue. And especially we want quality fabric and well-constructed garments that look good, and last.

We're not talking about going back in time to when tea dresses meant what they implied, and women never wore trousers in a golf club. Nor do we want to go back to formal ways of dressing when dress codes were the norm. We still value our wonderful clothes choice, and the freedom to wear what we like.

We definitely don't want more dictated formality. But in the twenty-first century why can't designers give more than a token thought to what we, of the wise years, really want? The fashion industry hasn't quite got it that mature fashion can be exciting, and lucrative! We want to be stylish, and want to part with our money – if we see flattering, well made, and unfrumpish clothes. There's a big gap in the market for a more imaginative look at what we young-at-hearters really want – with cut, quality and price in mind. And manufacturers forget to their peril that our group, as a demographic is growing rapidly. Between 2015 and 2020 the UK population is expected to grown by 3%, and over sixty-fives by 12%. Half the population by 2020 will be over fifty.

In particular, we would love many more dresses to choose from. I've heard this often from so many of my contemporaries. Dresses, we're always being told by the fashion press, are the easiest 'go-to' pieces. You add shoes, a piece of jewellery or scarf, and that's it. But where are they? Most are in gaudy colours, one shoulder in, the other out, displaying too much cleavage, or with thigh-creeper skirts you daren't sit down in. Or they have so many ruffles, sequins or wildly strobing stripes, that you want to cover your eyes. The ones we crave aren't frou-frou, frumpy or overly ornate, but have simple shapes, interesting but clean-cut necklines, long or three-quartered sleeves, and skirts of knee or below-the-knee length in quality fabric that doesn't crease too much.

There's also a shortage of well-priced jackets. I remember twenty or twenty-five years ago, you could find fitted jackets in every colour, fabric and style. I used to have rails of them in my shop, and remember well that if you found the right one it could transform your posture by adding a bit of structure to your shoulder. You looked better, and stood better. We need more of these.

Are we asking for the moon! I can't believe these requests are too extreme. I suspect what's missing is will of the designer who is still trapped in the 'young' time warp. Are they so fixed in Young Culture, that they fear any straying off piste will pollute the brand?

Can I hear some murmurings? Is someone saying that I've already sung the praises of 'new classic' garments, at affordable prices, in some boutiques and online sites. Yes. Quite right. But new classic tends to have contemporary twists in terms of cut, or fabric or decoration, and there isn't much to please those who love a neater and more fitted silhouette, and certainly not the superb cut of celebrity chic.

So there's celebrity chic that we would love, but the purse strings aren't stretchy enough. So how to find the clothes to transform us from cygnets to swans.

There's nothing for it but to grit your teeth (or surrender happily) to visiting lots of shops to find what you really want. But there'll be pleasure as well as sweat, I promise. Here we go…

WHERE TO GO

1

The Joy of Shopping

Aladdin's Cave

*I very, very rarely get the opportunity to go shopping
and actually feel the clothes and try things on.*
— Victoria Beckham

Shopping for clothes should be fun. It should be emotional. You're always on the edge of falling in love. Around the next corner, the next rack, could be the one item that's going to transform your life. Well, that's what it feel like at the time.

You step inside the door of a dress shop you've never visited before. If the owners have got it right, you're dazzled by the décor designed to make the clothes centre stage, and the newish or slight perfume of the clothes hanging before you. Every rail teeming with the possibility of transformation. The colours and textures leap out at you and you want to touch and be entranced by the fabrics. Be seduced by the new colours. It's a tempting fairyland.

It's a joy. Shopping for clothes is a great day out, especially if you're prepared to talk and listen to women around you. If you're trying on clothes at home, twisting and turning to see if you stick out anywhere you shouldn't, all you might get is an occasional grunt from your partner, 'Yes, that looks lovely,' when you know it probably doesn't.

Although clothes that flatter and fit the older woman are in short supply, especially in the high street where skinny teenage display mannequins act as magnets to entice young customers, there're shops, independently owned, which offer us exciting fashion. Let's visit one and get a feel for what they offer.

Blue, Saffron Walden

Saturday is market day in Saffron Walden, and buzzes with energy. I was visiting on a showery day, and it was still buzzing with vitality. People were weaving in and out of tented stalls, picking up a bargain here, having a taster of olives there, and loading up baskets with veg for the week. Close by, shops were displaying sausages of every size, shape and flavour, handicrafts, antiques, cosmetics, and groceries and, what I was looking for, fashion that I could drool over.

Blue, in King Street (www.bluesaffronwalden.co.uk) was as bubbly as the town itself. Amanda, who was managing the shop that day, was looking after three customers at once, looking like she could easily juggle three more. And the clothes glowed with colour and style that made the senses hum. I could see in an instant that there was a turquoise linen dress I had seen online, and lots more inviting things that I would like to try. Customers and staff were laughing and chatting about everything and nothing as they moved along the rails.

Amanda, outside *Blue* boutique, in Saffron Waldron.

And as I looked around the shop lots of different styles caught my eye. Colourful and monochrome, tops, dresses, jackets and coats that could mix with each other to make different outfits There were outfits perfect for a special occasion, and many more to lift your spirits on any day of the week.

I enjoyed talking to customers and staff about the town and what it had to offer, and why people loved coming to this shop. And, of course, about clothes and style and what I, and they, were looking for. I tried on lots of clothes, and got opinions from customers, the staff and the friend I was shopping with.

This is the hands-on shopping experience you don't get from

a magazine or laptop. The owner of the shop, Hayley, knows she and her team have to take special care of their customers, when so much on the high street or online is impersonal. 'If a customer sees something she would like to try on, but she only has enough time on Sunday, I'll come in for a few hours especially for her,' says Amanda, the manager.

It's their policy to involve themselves in the town, be part of the community, by having three charity fashions shows a year. They've an interactive website, which also offers click and collect.

All this is impressive as I well know from having run a fashion shop. To make it work, a small boutique has to work twenty-four-seven to find new styles, to offer them in shop and online, and have a presence in the town that's accessible and friendly.

The buzz from a good shopping outing can be addictive, and many women get hooked and their credit cards hijacked. Even we sensible ones (me included, of course) sometimes get brainwashed by what the fashion editors say is the latest colour, or the newest 'must have'. So for us, and especially recovering shopaholics, some reigning back of the endorphins is necessary when it comes to making the hard-headed decisions of what, and how much to buy. Wrong choices can haunt you for years. The right ones can give pleasure for ever.

It must be 'one day at a time'! Take a deep breath and know that fashion, the latest offerings of designers and magazine editors, isn't style. Think SLOW. See, Love, Ogle… and Wait!

This is the number-one shopping tip. Take your time shopping. Rushing a decision because your partner is pacing outside, or you're desperate for caffeine or sugar, brings many a disaster to your wardrobe. Look at what you might buy from all angles. Check if it's really comfortable and not pulling anywhere. Is the length right and if not, is it alterable? Is the fabric, whether summer or winter weight, thick enough to drape well and not cling? Take the garment to the window and see if the colour is what you think it is. Light makes a huge difference to how a colour appears.

If something makes you smile as soon as you put it on – it's probably right. But… it's still a good idea to go and have a coffee and think about it. First impressions aren't always right. The lighting in the shop might be too flattering – and mirrors can lie! We may be shopping after a lunchtime glass of wine when everything looks better. We might find something that's almost right, ie wrong, and we go ahead and buy anyway. Or, after a long search, we may be desperate to find something – just anything – to buy to make all the effort worthwhile.

With SLOW always in mind, shopping should be a joyous success. However, here are reminders of other tips you may have read before (boring!) but are still worth going over again.

- **Have a Plan.** Work out what kind of garment, or clothes, you're looking for – something casual and comfortable for every day, or something a tad different to wear when meeting friends. You also need an idea of the mood and colour you want. If you go with the attitude, 'I'll know it when I see it,' you'll never find anything.
- **Always think 'outfit'** – not 'that's such a pretty piece it's sure to go with something'. Make sure, when you're tempted to buy

any bottom or top, you know what you're going to wear it with. This was a lesson I learnt years ago when I ran a fashion shop, and a very elegant lady of mature years said she never bought individual pieces. It always had to be an outfit or a garment that would team up with something in her wardrobe to make an outfit. At the time, I thought how short sighted! She must be missing out on lots. But now I realise not only does it make style sense, it makes life easier.

- **Organise your wardrobe into outfits** (accessories attached, or nearby) then with just one grab, you've chosen for the day.
- **Remember your colour scheme,** and only buy pieces that fit in.
- **Stick to a neutral shade for the main pieces** in your wardrobe. It makes everyday dressing easier because more things can be worn together. You can work around blues, or beiges, or greys and if you keep to the same tones in most of your tops and bottoms, they'll mix together, and one main summer and winter coat will top them all.
- **Simplicity of line is always more elegant, more chic.** And it makes creating a total look easier. There're less bits and pieces to take account of. Don't be tempted by over-decorated pieces, even though they may be works of beautiful art in themselves.
- **Make sure things fit well.** Sounds obvious, but too tight makes us look fatter. Slightly body-skimming is far more slimming. I bet you can remember lots of times when you thought you could easily lose a bit of weight, or pretended you didn't see the bulges on your backside. And if you aren't a standard size, and few of us are, then look around for a good dressmaker. It's frustrating to have to pass by an otherwise perfect dress just because it's too long.

- **Choose quality fabrics.** Don't go for cheap cottons or linens that crease just by being breathed on. You can still wear good-quality natural fabrics in the summer, although they'll crease to some extent. You don't want the 'just run through a wheatfield' look. Look for fabrics that have some body and will keep their shape, and even mould your contours rather than your contours moulding them.

- **And don't forget polyester** – the first synthetic invented in 1941 that never wrinkles and comes out of the washing machine like new. Not good when the weather is hot, but for Tupperware (this brand still exists!) skies, or chilly evening occasions it keeps you looking uncreased and svelte.

- **Make sure you shop for important things on a good day.** If you're in a bad mood nothing will look right (or everything will, to compensate!) Maybe some retail window shopping will cheer you up, but save big purchases for a day when you feel positive.

- **Be resolute.** If the shop assistant is too pushy, stand your ground. Take a friend to help you resist a rush of blood to the head which is driving you to spend more on a scarf than a winter coat. If you're dithering, it's probably not for you.

- **Get out of your comfort zone.** Try things on that you like on others, but have never worn yourself. That's what hands-on shopping is all about – finding new things that might transform you. You never know till you try.

- **Take a fashion-savvy friend.** This is good for two reasons. She'll tell you honestly if something suits. And even if it does, but costs a fortune, she'll rein you back if she's been well-briefed before.

Now, here's what not to do. We may think we know it all – but how many mistakes have we made in our lifetime of shopping! These are some of the reasons why, so they're worth thinking about.

- **See a cut-price bargain. Buy it. Instantly.** At home, we've probably got something identical. It's so, so common to get into a rut and choose the same shape or colour over and over again. And we do know that a bargain isn't a bargain if it's never worn.

- **Never guess at colours.** If you want to match or blend a shade with a particular piece of clothing, take the garment itself with you. It's pretty nigh impossible to carry a precise tone in your head.

- **Don't be fooled by a shop display.** The clothes combination might look brilliant on the mannequin, but it doesn't mean it'll look the same on you. We're all so different that straight copying usually isn't an option. It's like with hair styles. It can be a big mistake to take a picture of a celebrity's hair style for your hairdresser to copy. It won't look the same, because you aren't the same!

- **Avoid anything that needs arranging.** If the minute you put something on it doesn't sit well – the drape doesn't work unless you pull it up, down or sideways, or when you sit everything falls apart, or the cross-over bit at the top keeps falling off your shoulder – don't buy it. A garment should be good-to-go as we're so often told, from the instant we get it over our head. And if something is said to be worn in six different ways, forget it. Even if you're shown the six variations in the shop, you'll forget five of them when you get home. It's like a washing machine, or any other machine come to think of it, that gives you 101 functions that you never use. Things can get too complicated.

- **As you get older, don't go darker, at least not often.** Yes, it's okay to have some black or navy in your wardrobe but remember that clear, fresh colours are more flattering to the duller skin. White is also good, even brilliant white suits most older women.
- **Avoid rough utility fabrics** – heavy denims and linens, and the military look that we probably loved in our youth. Smoother fabrics are more flattering because they make our complexions look… smoother.
- **Forget lacy material.** When worn near the face, it emphasises any 'lacy' wrinkles and lines.

I hope this chapter has rekindled your past enjoyment in buying clothes, or given you more reasons to engage in your still-vibrant passion for shopping.

And to encourage you to seek out small local shops, here's more on the 'independent' shopping experience that I have always loved.

2

Independent Shops
Places to Call Our Own

Whoever said money can't buy happiness simply didn't know where to go shopping.

— Bo Derek, American actor

I was walking around Cirencester last summer with my husband, intending to do 'Walk 10' of the town trails when a shop window display stopped me in my tracks. Through an open door I caught a glimpse of intriguing clothes and was drawn, helplessly (few men know this sense of total helplessness!), into the shop.

Seconds before, my husband had been eyeing up the facade of the old building and about to give me some information on the imposing Victorian frontage, when I realised that this was the corn hall, recently refurbished to provide shops, cafes and a theatre.

Just a peep inside Sue Parkinson's Cirencester boutique was enough to draw me in.

By a stroke of luck there was also a bookshop and a bistro for Derek, so I was released, temporarily, from our walk, and was able to explore the tempting retail venue of *Sue Parkinson* (www.sue-parkinson.com).

In I went, amid the gentle cacophony of soft music and people chatter, excited at finding a new and promising dress shop. And indeed it did not disappoint. The spacious interior was lit from natural daylight through arched windows and from spotlights on the high ceiling of the Victorian room. Rails upon rails of clothes were arranged closely, but not too closely so that you had plenty of space to wander in and out of the two large, interconnected rooms. With a mix of contemporary classic, grown-up funky, as well as quirky casual clothes, this was a perfect place for would-be STYLE STARS.

And, the reassuring and wonderful thing was that there were clothes for all ages, but lots for us grown-ups – outfits that were chic without being too short or clingy, feminine without being fussy, and edgy without being crazy. It was like coming home, being able to wander around a fashion shop, brushing shoulders with young, and older women, all sharing the same aim of finding something new to wear.

This was a place, like most independent shops, that we can call our own, a place where we young-at-hearters are on the same shopping field as twenties and thirties. Many outfits here would all look good on all of us, irrespective of our actual ages. There's no skulking around here as if we don't belong.

Sue's labels are always being reviewed and updated, so I won't be specific about the brands I saw then, but there will always be a mix of contemporary fashion for all ages.

On their 2017 autumn website there were lovely funky knits, silk and satin blouses, glamorous *Ana Alcazar* party and occasion

Sue's Broadway shop has similar, chic ranges to Cirencester and is a joy to visit.

dresses (www.a-n-a.com) as well as smart sweat pants and shirts, and *Maison Scotch* (www.scotch-soda.com) puffer jackets that could be teamed with sporty or smart trousers. Styles for us all.

Like all independent boutiques, this isn't a place where you have to fight your corner to get a close look at the clothes or pile into a communal changing room. This is where you can enjoy the process of shopping, take time to look, and get advice from the staff if you want it.

In addition to the boutique in Cirencester, Sue owns another dress shop in Broadway, Worcestershire, which has a similar aesthetic, many of the same labels, and is also a joy to visit.

Another charming independent boutique, *Jolie and Beau*, in Pershore, Worcestershire (www.jolieandbeau.co.uk) is well worth a visit if you're near the cathedral city, or visiting the north Cotswolds. It's owned and managed by Judy, aged sixty-one, who loves contemporary fashion, and thinks there're plenty of gorgeous clothes for those of us who are slightly older. She stands back, or will advise us if we want help.

Here are her guidelines for us young oldies. First off, make the most of your best feature. Be sensible and don't display your less than lovely parts.

- If you've good shoulders, wear an off-the-shoulder top, if you've good legs, get them out. Nothing should be ruled out.
- Choose a clean neckline. A v-neck is good for a big bust, and a soft round neckline suits most women.
- Don't try to hide your neck, or wear high polos. A medium-length long necklace will distract from your neck. But don't show too much flesh or go for too low a cleavage.

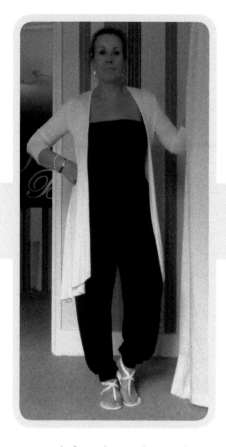

Judy, the owner of *Jolie and Beau* at Pershore, Worcestershire, always dresses with style.

And if you have a big, or bigger than before, tummy (and which of us don't) or generous hips, go for styles that skim the body, and don't cling.

Two labels which Judy now has in her shop are particularly good for us young-at-hearters. They are *Linda Ralso*n and *Grizas*.

Travelling around the country looking for clothes to love, I had very soon realised that high-voltage shopping centres and heaving high streets, left me dizzy. Too much of the same, too many people trying to get at too many rails. No room to try on – even if you found something half promising. And although I had known before I started writing this book that finding flattering clothes for us young-at-hearters would be a tough call, I hadn't reckoned on the amount of time and dogged determination it takes to trawl the aisles to find just one thing that makes the heart leap... and also fits!

So I soon narrowed down the search and concentrated on small shops in small- and medium-sized towns. Although I'd owned and run my own shop for many years, I hadn't quite appreciated how many other high-quality independents there are throughout the country. Most are small, although a few have expanded outwards and upwards over the years. If you are visiting somewhere new google fashion shops, and you will find them.

Each is unique in its own way. Their stock will vary from one to another depending on the personal style of the owner. Their emphasis might be on relaxed or glamorous, sporty or minimalistic, trendy or elegant, or all of the above. But, most importantly, they welcome us, and all age groups with open arms.

Most independent boutiques say they cater for thirty-five years upwards, but many admit that many of their clients are older than this. The owners are offering an alternative to the high street chains, and are always looking for individual clothes, not the same repetitive mix as in the big malls. And they don't insult us young-at-hearters with fuddy-duddy ranges, safe colours and easy-fit slacks. They choose contemporary brands that aim to be different from the high street, and that suit all ages. That isn't to say every garment on display suits everyone who comes through the door. Of course not. We're all different. But there will be something there for everyone.

Away from the crowds of the high street, and the domed auditoria of shopping centres, independents offer a relaxed space, under one roof, where you can get advice on how to put outfits together, and have plenty of time to try on.

And in the smaller shop you get to talk to people. They are venues for meeting other like-minded women to talk to about clothes and other things. That's what we women like to do. We talk about our lives, our passions and disasters, as well as our clothes. We converse, and learn about each other, and get help about clothes that suit us. This is exactly what I did when I travelled around exploring boutiques and what brands they had to offer. I looked at clothes, and talked to stylish women and asked them how they did it.

A study in 2017 by Liberis, a UK alternative finance provider, said that 8 out of 10 consumers planned to use independent businesses in preference to large chains this year, because they liked the personal service, and also wanted to support the local community.

On our style journey we have visited lots of independents because they're the perfect shopping destinations for us. But we should also remember they need us just as we need them in these cash-strapped times. There has been a lot said for many years about ever-rising rents and rates that are driving many small shops (and even some big chains) out of business. If we use them more, there will be more coming on stream to give us the style we deserve.

Online sites are here to stay, and many are increasingly efficient, and we all deserve the comfort of home shopping from time to time. But never forget proper independents. They should always be our first port of call.

TYING IT
ALL UP

1

To Rebel, or Not to Rebel, that is the Question

The Legacy of Diana Vreeland

A little bad taste is like a nice splash of paprika.
We all need a splash of bad taste—
it's hearty, it's healthy, it's physical.
I think we could use more of it. No taste is what I'm against.
    – Diana Vreeland, the late American columnist,
        fashion editor and author

Vreeland was the first rebel fashionista. It was she who, in the mid-twentieth century, began to change the idea of fashion from uniformity (what *ladies should* wear) to creativity (what *women can*

Diana Vreeland - who altered the
course of fashion in the twentieth
century. 1978 ©Lynn Gilbert.

choose to wear). She said it was not for fashion editors to tell women
what polite society was wearing, but it was for women themselves
to decide – to invent their own style.

And if any message in this book should get through – this is
the one. The way forward is to be your own person – even if this
sometimes makes you a rebel – and not to be afraid to express
opinions, and to dress with pizzaz as the mood takes you.

Diana Vreeland was our first STAR – she revelled in all of its principles.

Surprise
True to ourselves
Artistry
Reinvention

In *Harper's Bazaar* 1936 Vreeland had a 'Why Don't You?' column
which was radical, new and anti-current fashion. It gave tips not
intended to dictate but inspire, which were unusual, decadent, or
even absurd at the time.

- Wear a bowler?
- Stick Japanese hair-pins in your hair?
- Buy a transparent evening coat?
- Or bright flannel gloves?
- Or a black blouse?
- Hide your hips under an accordion-pleated jacket?
- Wear fruit hats?

She pointed to what some would call bad taste, but others would take as thought-provoking. Her message was do your own thing, don't follow the crowd. Be a rebel.

And, like Cleopatra, she was no conventional beauty. Her face was too long and her nose crooked, but she knew how to make the most of her looks and, with her drive and vision, she changed the sartorial world. It was the unusual in a person's features that was attractive, she believed, like Barbra Streisand's 'Nerfertiti' nose, Penelope Tree's doe-eyed, doleful face, the gap between Lauren Hutton's teeth and Mick Jagger's plump lips. Imperfections are things to be admired because they make us individual and human.

We have explored far and wide, but now we've got it. Good style is to have the courage to create a look for ourselves that's completely our own, tapping into the spirit of adventure we had when we were thirty. We have the choice to rebel, or not to rebel. But my money is on rebellion, if, like Diana Vreeland, that means you have to stand up for what you believe – and wear what is **surprisingly, artistically true to yourself,** with always **a nod to the new** – and not dictated to by the fashion industry.

Being a rebel is recognising that life is always moving forward, and that we should not shy away from the challenges that come with that. We knew that when we were young, even though changes probably swept us along too quickly then. But it's no different for us. The world moves relentlessly on. High tech becomes low tech. Smart no longer means street wise, but making use of the latest technology – smart TVs, smart homes. Vacuum cleaners go around the house all by themselves, and then put themselves to bed. Washing machines will do everything except fold up the clothes and put them away.

We have to adapt to the times. From time to time we have to reinvent ourselves. And so we should when it comes to personal style. We will then surprise others, and probably ourselves.

A previous customer of mine, Amelia, liked neat structured suits. The vogue had long switched from formal to casual, and fitted suits were hard to find. But find them Amelia did, because she liked them, and they suited her figure. 'Even if I'm going to the supermarket I put on a smart two-piece. It makes me look good, and I feel good.' She did not follow fashion rigidly, but she was wonderfully stylish. She was her own person. A rebel.

Our makeup expert, Jill, was always a rebel. 'It started when I preferred throwing baby rugby balls to dressing up dolls, and I think that an independent spirit helps you find your own style. And it's even more important when you're an older woman. You don't want to be invisible. You still want to be treated as any other woman, who has valuable opinions and wants to be listened to…' She's always looking for new projects, and always looking to update her wardrobe.

Janet, our international trade expert, says that as we get older we can be bolder in what we say. 'I'm a loose cannon now. I don't care what people think. I used to be very circumspect in what I said because I wanted people to like me. Now I can say things more freely. For example when I'm teaching export skills to business people, I'm now not afraid to enthuse about how fascinating I find this subject. Previously I had held back, because most people think exporting is boring, boring!'

My rebels think for themselves. They've learnt that rules (certainly fashion ones) are sometimes too rigid for their own good and need to be broken. They're forward thinkers.

But we should remember that bad taste, just like good taste, can and does change with the seasons. By today's standards, most of Vreeland's tips would be thought original not 'bad taste'. And would you ever have thought a few years ago that bejeweled, eye-wateringly expensive trainers would be applauded on the catwalk? Would you have ever put fuchsia and orange together in one outfit? Vulgarity and beauty are what we make of them at any particular time.

But also let's not forget that Vreeland was suggesting only 'a little splash' of bad taste. She was not saying go crazy with loads of it. A touch of vulgarity, if it's artistically presented, will end up as part of a beautiful picture.

And her message that we should look for the unusual and individual (surprising) and make it part of our personal style, is absolutely what we should be doing, even though this will push most of us out of our comfort zones. Sabine Reichel, a US blogger, has said she can put an outfit together from a handkerchief, underpants, a belt, safety pins and spit. Our boundaries don't have to be stretched as much as this, but some widening of our horizons is an essential part of upping our style.

Being a rebel needs nerve, single-mindedness, and a splash of Diana Vreeland's bad taste to explore, and choose from, the glorious array of clothes on offer. We use fashion for inspiration, but don't let it dictate to us. We look, with young eyes, for new and exciting things that give us style and transform our lives, and we do it with the help of the four STAR principles.

2

Into the Future
Reasons to be Cheerful

It's a new era in fashion – there're no rules.
It's all about the individual and personal style,
wearing high-end, low-end, classic labels,
and up-and-coming designers all together.
— Alexander McQueen

Creating our own style is the key to the future. Originality, rather than following the fashion pack, will become the norm. Leading trend forecaster, Lidewij Edelkoort in her *Manifesto for the Next Decade* agrees.

New consumers, she says, are going to create and design their own wardrobes by sharing, renting, and mixing last year's basic with next years must-haves, happy with hand-me-down garments. 'They wear PJs in the daytime and furs in the summer. Men's hats with women's dresses. Just having fun with clothes,' says Edelkoort. They are going against the flow of fashion as we've known it, and aren't being dictated to by designers from on high, or getting caught up in every 'must-have' of the season.

Nearly-new shops, part of this 'originality', are thriving again. There're two brilliant ones near me, *Beetroot* in Stow-on-the-Wold and *The Attic* in Chipping Campden where I've bought fabulous bargains at a fraction of the original prices. A lot of the clothes in good nearly-new boutiques are actually new, having been discarded without being worn. And it's by choosing to buy designer brands at second-hand prices that we can afford to experiment and be creative.

And in the last few years there have been encouraging signs that we young-at-hearters are being taken more seriously in the world of clothes design, and cosmetics. Couture houses slip in the occasional seventy-plus model. In 2016, seventy-three-year-old Lauren Hutton stepped on to the catwalk with twenty-one-year-old Gigi Hadid on *Bottega Venetas* catwalk show in Milan.

Fashion magazines and catalogues, driven by a new appreciation of the older brigade, are becoming more age conscious. Centenarian Bo Gilbert, 'I dress for myself, not the boys,' was featured in Vogue's 100th anniversary edition, looking beautiful in fuchsia silk and jewels. The online company *Me & Em* regularly feature a stylish, older woman.

But this new appreciation of the older woman hasn't gone far enough. Bo was tucked away in the inside pages, with no life story or celebration of her long-lived life, and the majority of *Me & Em* models are young women of flawless facial and body proportions. And on the shop floor – even in our wonderful independent boutiques – retailers still say their profile woman is thirty-five or forty-five plus. Often you hear the phrase 'style for any age', but everyone pussy-foots around actually saying the words, fifty-year-old, sixty-year-old or, heavens forbid, seventy plus!

The analysis firm Verdict Retail sees over-fifties women overlooked as fashionable customers. Kate Ormrod, senior analyst, in 2016, said that the fifty-plus woman shopper is 'notoriously neglected', with few players 'actively catering to mature consumers'. She suggests that an important way forward is to use older models, and she's quite right, we do need lots more Bo Gilberts.

So is there hope for us young-at-hearters? Yes, of course. Change is just beginning and will continue. We've numbers on our side, and the fashion industry, although only giving us token status at the moment, is moving in our direction. We're not calling for a seismic shift from Young Culture to Old-and-Past-it Culture. We want our own, exciting slice of designers' imagination – more that we can wear, enjoy and be stylish in. And the market force is with us. We're a growing band, and would buy tons more if there were clothes in abundance that we felt special in.

And, throughout the book we've seen a sufficient supply of clothes that we love, if we're selective, to make us cheerful for the future. There are now some designers and manufacturers who have introduced more imaginative and flowing lines, longer skirts, easier cuts, bright and subtle colours, which are great for us, and our daughters.

Even at the top end of fashion the mood is softening. At the beginning of 2017, Victoria Beckham's collection moved on from her iconic body-con dresses to more fluidity, with the addition of roomy, light and airy sleeves, wide hemlines on dresses and trousers, and georgette skirts. There were cosy, easy-fit knit and georgette skirts, teamed with the wider-shouldered jackets of the eighties. Feminine crushed velvet and floral blouses and dresses with stretch. Where the mighty go the rest will follow.

And many more designers are catering for the larger as well as the stick-thin body. *Rohen Chen* now does plus-size styles, because of increasing customer demand, up to 26, and *James Lakeland* goes up to size 20 trousers and has lots of casual wear. The brands we've talked about in the chapter on 'unstructured' clothes are all easy-flow outfits that look good on any size.

Even the colossal cosmetics industry is also moving our way. The term 'anti-aging', associated before with age spots and other 'visible signs of aging' has been banned by leading advertisers. They've listened to Helen Mirren who said women shouldn't have to 'fight' aging, but want to look as good as possible for their age not always struggling to look younger.

The future looks good for us young-at-hearters, if we stay strong, and stick up for our rights.

And Remember!

We're only thirty inside so we can use our imagination, and live as if we are. This doesn't mean going all out for the reckless try-anything-once attitude, but believing that we can do most things if we really put our minds to it.

The present day is all we have. And it's all we've ever had. Make the most of every opportunity.

Greater wisdom and knowledge of people and the world, is ours. We can use this to take up new careers, or hobbies.

The aesthetics and sensuality of fashion is just as appealing now as it was in our youth, maybe even more. Texture, touch, visual charm are still there to enjoy. Colour and appreciation of detail can get more intense as we get older.

It's okay to be invisible. Occasionally. We don't always have to be on style duty, to stand out from the crowd. We're allowed our quiet days, sliding into old slippers, forgetting the world and our responsibilities in it. That's one of the pleasures of maturity, to sit back and watch the world when we want to.

And, there's infinite pleasure in looking good, whatever age we are. When I was younger I thought it would be impossible to enjoy wearing appealing clothes when youthful charms had disappeared. But that's just not the case. It remains a joy to shop, to choose, to put together outfits that flatter. Good style still catches the eye, and gives continuing pleasure to the wearer, and the admirer.

Style captivates us through our life. But for us young oldies it can be the gateway to amazing personal transformation. Let's stand together and fight for the clothes we want and our right to stay visible.

Now let's swap ideas on style for the young-at-heart.
@maggie9cox
#youngatheartstyle